REVISE FOR

Edexcel
GCSE MATHEMATICS

HIGHER

Keith Pledger   **David Kent**

D0306514

About this book

This book is designed to help you get your best possible grade in your Edexcel GCSE Mathematics examination. The authors are the Chair of Examiners and the Development Manager for Mathematics, and have a good understanding of Edexcel's requirements.

Revise for Edexcel GCSE: Higher covers key topics that are often tested in the Higher level exam papers, focusing mainly on grades A*, A and B. *Revise for Edexcel GCSE Mathematics: Intermediate* focuses mainly on grades B, C and D, whilst *Revise for Edexcel GCSE Mathematics: Foundation* is focused on Grades D, E and F.

You can use the book to help you revise at the end of your course, or you can use it throughout your course alongside the course textbook: *Edexcel GCSE Mathematics: Higher* which provides complete coverage of the syllabus.

Helping you prepare for your exam

To help you prepare, each topic offers you:

Key points to remember – These summarize the mathematical ideas you need to know and be able to use.

Worked examples and examination questions – help you understand and remember important methods, and show you how to set out your answers clearly.

Revision exercises – help you practice using important methods to solve problems. Past paper questions are included so you can be sure you are reaching the right standard, and answers are given at the back of the book so you can assess your progress.

Test yourself questions – help you see where you need extra revision and practice. If you do need extra help they show you where to look in the *Edexcel GCSE Mathematics: Higher* textbook.

Exam practice and advice on revising

Examination style practice paper – this paper at the end of the book provides a set of questions of examination standard. It gives you an opportunity to practice taking a complete exam before you meet the real thing.

How to revise – For advice on revising before the exam, read the **How to revise** section on the next two pages.

How to revise using this book

Making the best use of your revision time

The topics in this book have been arranged in a logical sequence so you can work your way through them from beginning to end. But **how** you work on them depends on how much time there is between now and your examination.

If you have plenty of time before the exam (at least 8 weeks) then you can **work through each topic in turn**, covering the key points and worked examples before doing the revision exercises and test yourself questions.

If you are short of time then you can **work through the Test yourself sections first** to help you see which topics you need to do further work on.

However much time you have to revise in, make sure you break your revision into short blocks of about 40 minutes, separated by five or ten minute breaks. Nobody can study effectively for hours without a break.

Using the Test yourself sections

Each test yourself section provides a set of key questions. Try each question:

If you can do it and get the correct answer then move on to the next topic. Come back to this topic later to consolidate your knowledge and understanding by working through the key points, worked examples and revision exercises.

If you cannot do the question, or get an incorrect answer or part answer then work through the key points, worked examples and revision exercises before trying the test yourself questions again. If you need more help, the cross-references beside each test yourself question show you where to find relevant information in the *Edexcel GCSE Mathematics: Higher* textbook.

Reviewing the key points

Most of the key points are straightforward ideas that you can learn: try to understand each one. Imagine explaining each idea to a friend in your own words, and say it out loud as you do so. This is a better way of making the ideas stick than just reading them silently from the page.

As you work through the book, remember to go back over key points from earlier topics at least once a week. This will help you to remember them in the exam.

Working on the worked examples

Read each question at the start of each worked example and think about what it is asking you to do. Try to work out which key point(s) you need to use, and how to answer the question before you look at the answer itself.

The answer will tell you which key point(s) to use. Read this again if you need to.

follow the working through carefully, making sure you understand each stage. The margin notes give useful information – make sure you read them.

Using the revision exercises

Tackle the revision exercises in the same way as the worked examples. If you need to, go back to the key points and worked examples to see which method to use.

If you are not sure what to do, look at the answer at the back of the book to see if this gives you a clue. (For example – units such as £, or a % sign will give you a hint.)

Try to set out your answers in a similar way to the worked examples, showing all the stages in your working. In an examination you can gain marks by doing this. If the examiner sees that you have the right method you may gain marks even if you make an error in a calculation.

Taking the practice exam

The Higher GSCE papers are one and a half hours long, so put aside one and a half hours when you know you will not be disturbed and try to do the practice exam all in one go. This will give you some idea of how you need to pace yourself when you do the real thing.

Usually the easier topics come first in the exam, so most people start at the beginning to gain confidence by answering questions successfully.

Also, you may have some favourite topics you want to get under your belt first, so look through the whole paper at the start to get a feel for all the questions to be covered.

Wherever you start, **read the questions carefully**. Many candidates lose marks because they haven't done this.

As for the revision exercises, show all the stages in your working. If a question has 4 marks then 1 or 2 of them will be for the answer and the rest for the method you have used.

After finishing the practice exam, check your answers. If an answer is incorrect, check through your method making sure you haven't made any errors in your working.

If you can't find your mistake, use the cross reference by each question as a guide to see what to review. If you still can't find your mistake, ask your teacher to help you.

There are two cross references for every question. The first one, in *italics*, refers to the old edition of the Higher GCSE text book; the second one refers to the new edition.

What to review

If your answer is incorrect:
review in the Higher book:

Unit 4, page 70
Unit 4, page 75

1 Simplifying algebraic expressions

Key points to remember

1 $x^m \times x^n = x^{m+n}$

For example, $3y^2 \times 2y^3 = 6y^{2+3} = 6y^5$

Remember x is the *base* and n is the *index* or *power* (plural *indices*)

2 $(x^m)^n = x^{mn}$

For example, $(x^2)^3 = x^{2 \times 3} = x^6$

3 $x^m \div x^n = x^{m-n}$

For example, $6^6 \div 6^2 = 6^{6-2} = 6^4$

4 $x^0 = 1$ when $x \neq 0$

5 $x^{-n} = \dfrac{1}{x^n}$

For example, $2^{-3} = \dfrac{1}{2^3} = \dfrac{1}{8}$

6 $x^{\frac{1}{n}} = \sqrt[n]{x}$,

For example, $16^{\frac{1}{2}} = \sqrt{16} = \pm 4$

7 $x^{\frac{m}{n}} = (\sqrt[n]{x})^m$ or $\sqrt[n]{x^m}$

For example, $16^{\frac{5}{4}} = (\sqrt[4]{16})^5 = (2)^5 = 32$

8 $\dfrac{1}{n} + \dfrac{1}{m} = \dfrac{m+n}{mn}$

9 An expression of the form $ax^2 + bx + c$, with $a \neq 0$, is called a quadratic in x.

10 To factorize $ax^2 + bx$ take out the Highest Common Factor.

For example, $4x^2 + 10x = 2x(2x + 5)$

11 To factorize $ax^2 + bx + c$, start by looking for two numbers whose product is ac and whose sum is b.

12 $x^2 - y^2 = (x - y)(x + y)$

13 $x^2 \pm 2ax + a^2 = (x \pm a)^2$

14 Completing the square gives
$$x^2 \pm 2bx = (x \pm b)^2 - b^2$$

Worked examination question 1 [E]

(a)   Simplify $x^4 \div x^{-3}$

(b)   Find the value of x for which $4^{\frac{x}{2}} = 32$

Answer

(a)   Using **3** $x^4 \div x^{-3} = x^{4--3}$

$$= x^7$$

> Remember $- - = +$

(b)   Using **7** $4^{\frac{x}{2}} = (\sqrt{4})^x$

$$= 2^x$$

Now $32 = 2 \times 2 \times 2 \times 2 \times 2 = 2^5$

Then $2^x = 2^5$

So $x = 5$

Worked examination question 2 [E]

Factorize completely $6x^2 + 9x$

Answer

Using **10** $6x^2 + 9x = 3x(2x + 3)$

Worked examination question 3 [E]

Simplify

$$\frac{1}{x+3} + \frac{1}{x-5}$$

Answer

Using **8** with $n = (x + 3)$ and $m = (x - 5)$

$$\frac{1}{x+3} + \frac{1}{x-5} = \frac{(x-5) + (x+3)}{(x+3)(x-5)} = \frac{2x-2}{(x+3)(x-5)}$$

Using **10**

$$= \frac{2(x-1)}{(x+3)(x-5)}$$

Worked examination question 4 [E]

(a)   Factorize $m^2 - n^2$

(b)   Rewrite 9991 as the difference of two squares.
     Hence find the prime factors of 9991.

Answer

(a)   Using **12** $m^2 - n^2 = (m + n)(m - n)$

(b)   Using **12** $9991 = 10\,000 - 9$

$$= 100^2 - 3^2$$
$$= (100 + 3)(100 - 3)$$
$$= 103 \times 97$$

$\therefore$ prime factors are 103 and 97.

Example 1

Factorize:

(a) $x^2 + 5x - 6$ (b) $6x^2 + 5x - 4$

Answer

(a) Using ⑪ $a = 1, b = 5, c = -6$
Then $ac = -6, b = 5$
Two numbers whose product is -6 and sum is 5 are -1 and 6.

$$-1 \times 6 = -6$$
$$-1 + 6 = 5$$

Therefore $x^2 + 5x - 6 = (x - 1)(x + 6)$

(b) Using ⑪ $ac = -24, b = 5$
This is best done by trial and error.

Try $(6x - 4)(x + 1)$
$$= 6x^2 + 6x - 4x - 4$$ ✗ (wrong)

Try $(2x - 1)(3x + 4)$
$$= 6x^2 + 8x - 3x - 4$$
$$= 6x^2 + 5x - 4$$ ✓ (right)

Example 2

(a) Complete the square on

$$x^2 - 10x + 32$$

(b) Find:

(i)   the minimum value of $x^2 - 10x + 32$
(ii)   the value of x for which this minimum occurs.

Answer

(a) By completing the square:

$$x^2 - 10x + 32$$
$$\Rightarrow \qquad (x - 5)^2 - 25 + 32$$
$$\Rightarrow \qquad (x - 5)^2 + 7$$

(b) (i)   Since the minimum value of $(x - 5)^2$ is 0;
then the minimum value of $(x - 5)^2 + 7$ is 7.
Hence the minimum value of $x^2 - 10x + 32$ is 7.

(ii)   This minimum occurs when $(x - 5)^2 = 0$
i.e. $x = 5$.

Example 3

Given that, for all values of x,

$$x^2 + 6x - 11 = (x + n)^2 + m$$

find the values of n and m.

Answer

Completing the square on

$$x^2 + 6x - 11$$

gives

$$x^2 + 6x - 11 \rightarrow (x+3)^2 - 9 - 11$$
$$\rightarrow (x+3)^2 - 20$$

So

$$(x+3)^2 - 20 \equiv (x+n)^2 + m$$

So $n = 3$ $m = -20$

> **Note**
> $\equiv$ means 'identically equal for all values of x^2.'

Example 4

Complete the square on

$$8x - x^2$$

Answer

$$8x - x^2 = -(x^2 - 8x)$$
$$- (x^2 - 8x) \rightarrow -[(x+4)^2 - 16]$$
$$\rightarrow -(x+4)^2 + 16$$
$$\rightarrow 16 - (x+4)^2$$

So $8x - x^2 = 16 - (x-4)^2$

Revision exercise 1

1 Write down the value of
   (a) $4^{1\frac{1}{2}}$ (b) $27^{-\frac{1}{3}}$ [E]

2 $y = 2^{-x}$
   (a) Calculate the value of y when $x = 0$
   (b) Calculate the value of y when $x = 3$ [E]

3       $x^2 \times x^3 = x^p$
   (a) Write down the value of p.
       $\sqrt{x} = x^q$
   (b) Write down the value of q.
       $(x^2 \times x^3) \div \sqrt{x} = x^r$
   (c) By expressing r in terms of p and q, or otherwise, find the
       value of r.   [E]

4 (a) Factorize completely $10x^2 - 5x$
   (b) Calculate the value of y, when $x^{\frac{1}{2}} \div x^{-3} = x^y$ [E]

5 Factorize completely
   (a) $6x^2y^2 - 3x^4y^2$ (b) $12xy^3 - 8x^4y$ [E]

6 Factorize completely $\quad ax - by - bx + ay$ $\qquad\qquad$ [E]

7 Simplify

(a) $a^4 \times a^5$ $\qquad\qquad$ (b) $(x^3)^2$ $\qquad\qquad$ (c) $3x^2 \times 4x^3$

(d) $x^9 \div x^5$ $\qquad\qquad$ (e) $6x^5 \div 2x^2$ $\qquad\qquad$ (f) $(\frac{1}{16})^{\frac{1}{2}}$

(g) $8^{\frac{5}{3}}$ $\qquad\qquad$ (h) $(4x^0)^5$ $\qquad\qquad$ (i) $27^{\frac{2}{3}}$

8 Write as a single fraction in its lowest terms

(a) $\dfrac{1}{x} + \dfrac{2}{y}$ $\qquad$ (b) $\dfrac{4}{3x} + \dfrac{5}{6x}$ $\qquad$ (c) $\dfrac{x}{2}\dfrac{1}{} + \dfrac{x+3}{6}$ $\qquad$ (d) $\dfrac{1}{x+2} - \dfrac{4}{x-1}$

9 Factorize

(a) $x^2 + 4x$ $\qquad\qquad$ (b) $2x^2y - 6xy^2$ $\qquad\qquad$ (c) $x^2 + 3x + 2$

(d) $x^2 - 5x + 4$ $\qquad\qquad$ (e) $x^2 + 7x - 8$ $\qquad\qquad$ (f) $x^2 + 12x + 32$

(g) $2x^2 + 5x + 2$ $\qquad\qquad$ (h) $15x^2 - 4x - 3$ $\qquad\qquad$ (i) $8x^2 - 14x + 3$

(j) $2x^4 + 7x^2 - 4$ $\qquad\qquad$ (k) $x^2 + 6x + 9$ $\qquad\qquad$ (l) $x^2 - 8x + 16$

10 Complete the square on:

(a) $x^2 + 12x$

(b) $10x - x^2$

11 Given that
$$x^2 - 7x + 13\tfrac{1}{4} = (x + p)^2 + q$$
for all values of x, find the value of p and q.

12 $y = x^2 + 8x + 19$

(a) Find the minimum value of y.

(b) Find the value of x for which y is a minimum.

Test yourself	What to review
	If your answer is incorrect, review in the Higher book:
1 Simplify $2x^5 \times 3x^2$	*Unit 20, Examples 1 and 2* Unit 20, Examples 1 and 2
2 Simplify $10x^6 \div 5x^3$	*Unit 20, Example 4* Unit 20, Example 4
3 Find the value of $(125)^{-\frac{2}{3}}$	*Unit 20, Examples 5 and 6* Unit 20, Examples 5 and 6
4 Write as a single fraction:	$\dfrac{3}{x+2} - \dfrac{1}{x+1}$

6 Simplifying algebraic expressions

Unit 20, Example 14
Unit 20, Example 14

Test yourself	What to review
	If your answer is incorrect, review in the Higher book:
5 Factorize $6x^2 + 8x$	*Unit 20, Example 17* Unit 20, Example 17
6 Factorize $x^2 - 5x + 4$	*Unit 20, Example 18* Unit 20, Example 18
7 Factorize $6x^2 + 11x - 10$	*Unit 20, Examples 19 and 20* Examples 19 and 20
8 Given that: $$x^2 - 8x + 21 = (x + a)^2 + b$$ for all values of x, find the values of a and b.	*Unit 21, Example 6* Unit 21, Example 6

Answers to Test yourself

1 $6x^7$ **2** $2x^3$ **3** $\frac{1}{25}$ **4** $\dfrac{2x+1}{(x+2)(x+1)}$ **5** $2x(3x+4)$ **6** $(x-1)(x-4)$ **7** $(3x-2)(2x+5)$

8 $a = -4, b = 5$

2 Basic number skills

Key points to remember

1 If an amount increases by $x\%$ the new amount is $(100 + x)\%$ of the original amount.

2 If an amount decreases by $x\%$ the new amount is $(100 - x)\%$ of the original amount.

3 Percentage change $= \dfrac{\text{increase or decrease}}{\text{original}} \times 100\%$

4 Compound interest is interest paid on an amount and on the interest on that amount.

You can use the formula $\quad A = P\left(1 + \dfrac{R}{100}\right)^{n}$

where P is the principal (amount lent or borrowed)
$\quad\quad R$ is the rate of interest (% p.a.)
$\quad\quad n$ is the number of years of the investment or loan
$\quad\quad A$ is the amount (principal $+$ compound interest) after n years

5 Average speed $= \dfrac{\text{distance travelled}}{\text{time taken}}$ (typical units: km/h)

6 Density $= \dfrac{\text{mass}}{\text{volume}}$ (typical units: kg/m^3)

7 You can use ratios such as $2:3$ and $5:4:7$ to show how quantities are divided or shared.

8 Large and small numbers can conveniently be represented in standard form:

$$a \times 10^{n}$$

where $1 \leqslant a < 10$ and n is an integer
For example,
$$7\,200\,000 = 7.2 \times 10^{6}$$
$$0.000\,135 = 1.35 \times 10^{-4}$$

9 To add or subtract fractions:
$$\frac{a}{b} \pm \frac{c}{d} = \frac{ad \pm bc}{bd}$$

10 To multiply fractions:
$$\frac{a}{b} \times \frac{c}{d} = \frac{a \times c}{b \times d}$$

11 To divide fractions:
$$\frac{a}{b} \div \frac{c}{d} = \frac{a}{b} \times \frac{d}{c} = \frac{a \times d}{b \times c}$$

Worked examination question 1 [E]

In 1990, a charity sold $2\frac{1}{4}$ million lottery tickets at 25p each.
80% of the money obtained was kept by the charity.

(a)   Calculate the amount of money kept by the charity.

In 1991, the price of a lottery ticket fell by 20%.
Sales of lottery tickets increased by 20%.
80% of the money obtained was kept by the charity.

(b)   Calculate the percentage change in the amount of money kept
by the charity.

Answer

(a)   Amount to charity $80\% = \dfrac{80}{100}$

Value of 80% of $2\frac{1}{4}$ million 25p tickets $= \dfrac{80}{100} \times 2\,250\,000 \times £0.25$

$$= £450\,000$$

(b)   Using **2**

new price of lottery ticket $= (100 - 20)\% = 80\%$ of old price

$$= \dfrac{80}{100} \times £0.25 = £0.20$$

Using **1**

increase of 20% in sales $= (100 + 20)\% = 120\%$

$$\therefore \quad \text{sales} = \dfrac{120}{100} \times 2\,250\,000$$

$$= 2\,700\,000 \text{ sales}$$

Amount to charity $= 2\,700\,000 \times £0.20 \times \dfrac{80}{100}$

$$= £432\,000$$

Using **3** $\% \text{ change} = \dfrac{\text{decrease}}{\text{original}} \times 100\%$

$$= \dfrac{(450\,000 - 432\,000)}{450\,000} \times 100\%$$

$$= 4\%$$

Example 1

Calculate the compound interest on £800 at 6.5% over 5 years.

Answer

Using **4** $A = P\left(1 + \dfrac{R}{100}\right)^{n}$

where $P = 800$
$R = 6.5$
$n = 5$

Then
$$A = 800\left(1 + \frac{6.5}{100}\right)^5 = \text{£1096.07 to the nearest penny.}$$

So the compound interest is £1096.07 − £800 = £296.07

Example 2
Work out the value of:

$$\frac{2\frac{3}{4} - 1\frac{1}{3}}{1\frac{1}{2} \times \frac{4}{5}}$$

Answer

$$2\frac{3}{4} \to \frac{11}{4} \qquad\qquad 1\frac{1}{3} \to \frac{4}{3}$$

$$2\frac{3}{4} - 1\frac{1}{3} \to \frac{11}{4} - \frac{4}{3} = \frac{11 \times 3 - 4 \times 4}{12} = \frac{33 - 16}{12} = \frac{17}{12}$$

$$1\frac{1}{2} \times \frac{4}{5} \to \frac{3}{2} \times \frac{4}{5} \to \frac{12}{10} \qquad \left(\text{or } \frac{6}{5}\right)$$

$$\frac{2\frac{3}{4} - 1\frac{1}{3}}{1\frac{1}{2} \times \frac{4}{5}} \to \frac{17}{12} \div \frac{12}{10} \to \frac{17}{12} \times \frac{10}{12} = \frac{170}{144} = \frac{85}{72}$$

$$= \frac{85}{72} \text{ or } 1\frac{13}{72}$$

Worked examination question 2 [E]
The speed of light is approximately 300 000 000 m/s.

(a)   Write 300 000 000 in standard index form.
(b)   Calculate the time, in seconds, light takes to travel 1 metre.
        Give your answer in standard index form.

Answer

(a)   Using **8**   where $a = 3$ and $n = 8$
$$3.0 \times 10^8 \text{ m/s}$$

(b)   Using **5**   time $= \dfrac{\text{distance}}{\text{speed}}$ ———————————— Remember to keep the units the same throughout the problem.

where distance $= 1$ metre, speed $= 3.0 \times 10^8$ m/s

$$\text{time} = \frac{1}{3.0 \times 10^8}$$

$$= 3.3 \times 10^{-9} \text{ seconds}$$

Example 3
Share 1320 in the ratio $5:4:3$

Answer
Using **7**   There are 12 parts so 1 part $= 1320 \div 12 = 110$
$\therefore$ 1320 is shared into: $5 \times 110 = 550$
$4 \times 110 = 440$
$3 \times 110 = 330$

Example 4
In the sales a shop reduces all prices by 20%.
The sale price of a coat is £50.
Calculate the original price of the coat.

Answers
Using **2**   the sale price $= (100 - 20)\% = 80\%$ of the original price.
$\therefore$ sale price $= 0.8 \times$ original price

$\therefore$ $\dfrac{\text{sale price}}{0.8} =$ original price

$\therefore$ original price $= \dfrac{£50}{0.8}$

$= £62.50$

Revision exercise 2

1 A suit is originally marked at a price of £240. It is later
   increased in price by 12%, then reduced in a sale by 25%.
   What is the sale price?

2 Calculate the compound interest on £8400 over 6 years at 7.3%.

3 Share £6600 in the ratio $8:4:3$

4 Work out the value of
   $$(4.6 \times 10^{-2}) \times (8.3 \times 10^{4})$$
   giving your answer in standard index form.   [E]

5 A building society is going to be sold for £1 800 000 000.
   (a) Write the number 1 800 000 000 in standard form.
   This money is going to be shared equally between the 2.5×10^{6}
   members of the building society.
   (b) How much should each member get?
   Later, 3×10^{5} members find out that they **will not** get a share of
   the money.
   (c) How many members **will** now receive a share of the money?
   Give your answer in standard form.   [E]

6 The diameter of an atom is 0.000 000 03 m.

  (a) Write 0.000 000 03 in standard form.

Using the most powerful microscope, the smallest objects that can be seen have diameters that are **one hundredth** of the diameter of an atom.

  (b) Calculate the diameter, in metres, of the smallest objects that can be seen using this microscope.
  Give your answer in standard form. [E]

7

> **KILLICK BANK**
>
> MONTHLY REPORT JUNE
>
> 147 million pounds was used
> to buy 2100 houses.
> Average cost of a house is £

  (a) Write the number 147 million in standard form.
  (b) Write the number 2100 in standard form.

The corner of the page showing the average cost of a house is missing.

  (c) Use your answers to **(a)** and **(b)** to calculate the average cost of a house.
  Give your answer in standard form. [E]

8 A large supermarket imports wine from France.
A box of 5 bottles of wine costs the supermarket 28 euros per box.
The supermarket sells the wine for £4.80 per bottle.
The exchange rate is 1.40 euros to the £.

  (a) Calculate the percentage profit made on each bottle.

The exchange rate changes to 1.12 euros to the £.

  (b) Calculate the new selling price per bottle so that the percentage profit remains the same. [E]

9 In the sales a department store reduces all prices by 25%.
The sale price of a dress is £69.
Work out the price of this dress before the sale.

10 The area of the Earth covered by sea is 362 000 000 km^2.

  (a) Write 362 000 000 in standard form.

The surface area, A km^2, of the Earth may be found using the formula

$$A = 4\pi r^2$$

where r km is the radius of the Earth.

$$r = 6.38 \times 10^3.$$

  (b) Calculate the surface area of the Earth.
  Give your answer in standard form, correct to 3 significant figures.

(c) Calculate the percentage of the Earth's surface which is covered by sea.
Give your answer correct to 2 significant figures.   [E]

11 Work out the exact value of

$$\frac{3\frac{2}{5} - 1\frac{3}{4}}{2\frac{1}{3} + \frac{3}{5}}$$

12 Work out the exact value of x^2, when $x = 2\frac{3}{7}$.

13 Work out the exact value of

$$\frac{\frac{4}{5} \div 1\frac{1}{4}}{1\frac{1}{3} + \frac{1}{5}}$$

Give your answer in its simplest form.

Test yourself	What to review
	If your answer is incorrect, review in the Higher book:
1 A car priced at £10 400 is increased by 4.5%, then reduced by 10% in the Easter sale. What is the cost of the car at Easter?	*Unit 5, Example 3 and 4* Unit 5, Example 3 and 4
2 A person invests £5000 at 6.6% compound interest over 5 years. What is the total amount after 5 years?	*Unit 5, Section 5.6* Unit 5, Section 5.7
3 Share £2400 in the ratio 6:4:2	*Unit 5, Example 12* Unit 5, Example 13
4 Work out $(4 \times 10^8) - (4 \times 10^6)$ Give your answer in standard form.	*Unit 5, Example 14* Unit 5, Example 15
5 Work out the exact value of: $$\frac{2\frac{4}{7} \times 1\frac{1}{4}}{3\frac{1}{4} - 1\frac{3}{5}}$$	*Unit 1, Section 1.10* Unit 1, Section 1.10

Answers to Test yourself

1 £9781.20   2 £6882.66   3 1200, 800, 400   4 3.96×10^8 5 $\frac{150}{77}$ or $1\frac{73}{77}$

3 Decimals, surds and π

Key points to remember

1 A terminating decimal occurs when the denominator
divides exactly into the numerator.
For example,

$$\tfrac{1}{8} = \tfrac{125}{1000} = 0.125$$

2 A recurring decimal occurs when the denominator divides
the numerator giving a repeating pattern.
For example,

$$\tfrac{2}{7} = 0.285\,714\,285\,714\ldots$$

The pattern is repeated
every 6 decimal places.

3 Numbers which have decimal parts that either terminate
or recur are called rational numbers.

They can be expressed as $\dfrac{a}{b}$ where a and b are integers.
For example,

$$5 = \tfrac{5}{1}, 0.25 = \tfrac{1}{4}, 0.66\dot{6} = \tfrac{2}{3}$$

An integer is a positive or
negative whole number,
including zero.

4 Irrational numbers cannot be written as fractions in the
form $\dfrac{a}{b}$ where a and b are integers.
For example:

$$0.232\,332\,333\ldots$$
$$\pi = 3.141\,592\,654\ldots$$

Square roots of prime
numbers are irrational.

Irrational numbers do not terminate or have any
recurring pattern.

5 The set of real numbers is the set of all rational numbers
together with the set of all irrational numbers.

6 The equation $x^2 = n$ has two solutions (provided $n > 0$).
These are:

$$x = +\sqrt{n} \qquad x = -\sqrt{n}$$
or $\qquad x = \pm\sqrt{n}$

7 If n is a whole number and not a perfect square, then
$\sqrt{n}$ is called a surd.

i.e. $\sqrt{3}, \sqrt{7}, \sqrt{15}$ are surds.

8 If $\sqrt{n}$ is a surd, then
$\dfrac{1}{\sqrt{n}} = \dfrac{\sqrt{n}}{n}$ and this is the rationalized form of $\dfrac{1}{\sqrt{n}}$.

Key points to remember

9   Sometimes we leave answers in terms of π,

i.e. the area of this circle is:

$$\pi \times 4^2 = 16\pi \,\text{cm}^2$$

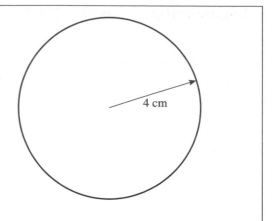

4 cm

Example 1

(a)   Rationalize the denominator of $\dfrac{1}{\sqrt{7}}$

Answer

$$\frac{1}{\sqrt{7}} \times \frac{\sqrt{7}}{\sqrt{7}} = \frac{\sqrt{7}}{7}$$

multiply top and bottom by $\sqrt{7}$

Answer

(b)   Express $\sqrt{6} \times \sqrt{8}$ in its most simplified surd form:

$$\sqrt{6} \times \sqrt{8} = \sqrt{48}$$
$$= \sqrt{3 \times 16}$$
$$= 4\sqrt{3}$$

Worked examination question 1 [E]

Write down the recurring decimal $0.\dot{4}\dot{8}$ in the form $\dfrac{a}{b}$, where a and b are integers.

Answer

Using **2** $0.\dot{4}\dot{8} = 0.48\,48\,48\ldots$

Let $x = 0.48\,48\,48\ldots$ (1)

Then $100x = 48.484\,848\ldots$ (2)

Multiply by a factor of 10 equivalent to the number of recurring digits.
Here, there are 2 recurring digits.
Multiply by $10^2 = 100$.

Then subtract (2) − (1)

$$100x - x = 48.484\,848\ldots - 0.484\,848\ldots$$
$$99x = 48$$
$$x = \tfrac{48}{99} = \tfrac{16}{33}$$

Therefore $0.\dot{4}\dot{8} = \tfrac{16}{33}$

Worked examination question 2 [E]

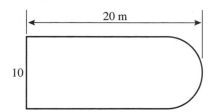

The diagram represents a swimming pool. The pool is rectangular
with a semi-circular end.
Work out the perimeter of the pool.
Leave your answer in terms of π.

Answer

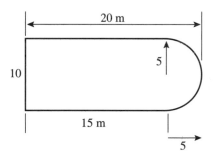

The perimeter is
$10 + 15 + 15 +$ circumference of semi-circle
$= 40 + \frac{1}{2} \times 2\pi r$

$= 40 + \pi \times r$
$= 40 + 5\pi$ m

Example 2

Write the decimal

$$0.4\dot{1}\dot{7}$$

in the form $\dfrac{a}{b}$ where a and b are integers.

Answer

$$0.4\dot{1}\dot{7} = 0.4 + 0.0\dot{1}\dot{7}$$
$$= \tfrac{4}{10} + 0.0\dot{1}\dot{7}$$

but $\qquad 0.\dot{1}\dot{7} = \tfrac{17}{99}$

so $\qquad 0.0\dot{1}\dot{7} = \tfrac{17}{990}$

so $\qquad 0.4\dot{1}\dot{7} = \tfrac{4}{10} + \tfrac{17}{990}$

$$= \frac{4 \times 99 + 17}{990}$$

$$= \frac{396 + 17}{990}$$

$$= \tfrac{413}{990}$$

Example 3

Solve the equation

$$x^2 + 2 = 29$$

Answer

Give your answer in its most simplified surd form.

$$x^2 + 2 = 29$$

so $x^2 = 29 - 2$

$x^2 = 27$

$x = \pm\sqrt{27}$

$x = \pm\sqrt{9 \times 3}$

$x = \pm 3\sqrt{3}$

Revision exercise 3

1 Rationalize:

(a) $\dfrac{1}{\sqrt{5}}$

(b) $\dfrac{1}{2\sqrt{7}}$

2

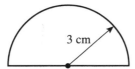

3 cm

The diagram represents a semi-circle of radius 3 cm.
Work out the area of the semi-circle.
Leave your answer in forms of π.

3 (a) Express

$$0.4\dot{2}\dot{7}$$

as a fraction in the form $\dfrac{a}{b}$.

(b) Express $0.3\dot{2}\dot{6}$

as a fraction in the form $\dfrac{a}{b}$.

4 Solve the equation

$$x^2 - 3 = 47$$

giving your answer in its most simplified surd form.

5 Every rational number can be written as a fraction $\dfrac{a}{b}$
where a and b are integers.

When　　　　$x = 0.919\,191\ldots$
then　　　　$100x = 91.9191\ldots$
(a) **(i)** Work out the value of $99x$.
　　　(ii) Write down x as a fraction $\dfrac{a}{b}$ where a and b are integers.
(b) Write down a positive rational number which is less than x.　　　　　　　　　　　　　　　　[E]

6 Prove that

$$\frac{1}{\sqrt{7}} + \frac{1}{\sqrt{3}} = \frac{3\sqrt{7} + 7\sqrt{3}}{21}$$

Test yourself	What to review
	If your answer is incorrect, review in the Higher book:
1 $x^2 - 4 = 68$ Solve the equation, giving your solution in its most simplified surd form.	*Unit 21, Example 4* Unit 21, Example 4
2 Express $0.1\dot{3}\dot{7}$ as a fraction in the form $\dfrac{a}{b}$	*Unit 23, Examples 3, 4, 5* Unit 23, Examples 3, 4, 5
3 Rationalize: $\dfrac{1}{3\sqrt{7}}$	Unit 23, Example 9

Answers to Test yourself

1 $6\sqrt{2}$　**2** $\frac{137}{999}$　**3** $\frac{\sqrt{7}}{21}$

4 Upper and lower bounds

Key points to remember

1 If you make a measurement correct to a given unit the true value lies in a range that extends half a unit below and half a unit above the measurement
Sometimes these are called the *greatest* **lower bound** and the *least* **upper bound**.

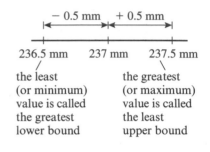

the least (or minimum) value is called the greatest lower bound

the greatest (or maximum) value is called the least upper bound

2 The greatest lower bound and the least upper bound are the minimum and maximum possible values of a measurement or calculation.

3 The absolute error is the difference between the measure's value and the actual value of a quantity.

4 The percentage error is found by converting the fraction

$$\frac{\text{absolute error}}{\text{actual value}} \text{ into a percentage.}$$

Worked examination question 1 [E]

On the scales in Ali's bookshop the weight of a book correct to 2 decimal places is 0.62 kg.

(a) Write down
   (i) the lower bound of the weight of the book.
   (ii) the upper bound of the weight of the book.

Ali needs to work out the weight of 50 copies of the book. He uses his value for the weight of one book.

(b) Calculate
   (i) the lower bound of the weight of 50 books,
   (ii) the upper bound of the weight of 50 books.
(c) Calculate the greatest possible error that could occur in calculating the weight of 50 copies of the book.
(d) Write down the greatest possible error that could occur in calculating the weight of 500 copies of the book.

Answer

(a) (i) Using **1**
      lower bound = 0.62 − 0.005
              = 0.615 kg
  (ii) Using **1**
      upper bound = 0.62 + 0.005
              = 0.625 kg

(b) (i) lower bound 50 books $= 50 \times$ lower bound
$$= 50 \times 0.615$$
$$= 30.75\,\text{kg}$$
    (ii) upper bound 50 books $= 50 \times$ upper bound
$$= 50 \times 0.625$$
$$= 31.25\,\text{kg}$$

(c) Greatest possible error
$$= \text{upper bound 50 books} - \text{Ali's value for 50 books}$$
$$= 31.25 - 31$$
$$= 0.25\,\text{kg}$$

(d) Greatest possible error 500 books $= 0.25 \times 10$
$$= 2.5\,\text{kg}$$

Example 1

The weight of a bag of sugar should be 1 kg but it is found to have
a weight of 1.15 kg.
Calculate the percentage error.

Answer

Using **3** the absolute error $= 1.15 - 1$
$$= 0.15$$

Using **4** the percentage error $= \dfrac{0.15}{1.15} \times 100\%$
$$= 13\%$$

Worked examination question 2 [E]

$$y = \frac{x + 30}{x}$$

$x = 20$, correct to 1 significant figure.
Work out the upper bound for y.

Write:

$$y = \frac{x + 30}{x}$$

$$y = \frac{x}{x} + \frac{30}{x}$$

$$y = 1 + \frac{30}{x}$$

The upper bound for y will occur when $\dfrac{30}{x}$ is as large as possible,

i.e. when x is as small as possible.

The smallest possible value for x is 15.

So $\quad y\,\text{max} = 1 + \dfrac{30}{15}$

$$= 1 + 2$$

$$= 3$$

Revision exercise 4

1 Sarah timed a 100 metre race using a stop watch. The time of the winner was 12.6 seconds. The stop watch can measure correct to the nearest one fifth of a second.
(a) Write down the lower bound and the upper bound for the actual time, in seconds.

An electronic timing mechanism gave a time of 12.56 seconds.

(b) State whether this time agrees with that of the stop watch, giving a reason for your answer. [E]

2 A stone is dropped down a well and hits the bottom after t seconds.
The depth of the well, s, is given by the formula
$$s = 4.905 \times t^2$$
(a) When $t = 2.5$ seconds (measured to the nearest 0.1 second) calculate
   (i) the maximum depth of the well, given by the formula,
   (ii) the minimum depth of the well, given by the formula.
(b) Write down the value of s correct to an appropriate degree of accuracy. [E]

3 The area, correct to 3 significant figures, of a large rectangular car park is 27 500 square metres. The breadth, correct to 3 significant figures, is 155 metres.
(a) Find the possible values of the area and breadth. Use these values to calculate the greatest and smallest length of the car park and hence copy and complete the inequality:

$$\ldots\ldots < \text{length} < \ldots\ldots$$

(b) To how many significant figures are your two answers the same? [E]

4 The area of a circle is found by using the formula
$$A = \pi r^2$$

The radius of a circle was measured wrongly as 4.5 cm.
Then its area was calculated.

The correct measurement of the radius was 4.6 cm.
(a) Work out the error in the calculated area.

Approximations for π include $\frac{22}{7}$, 3.142 and 3.14.
The π button of a calculator is often used instead of these numbers.
A circle has a radius of 4.600 cm, correct to 3 decimal places.
(b) Calculate the upper and lower bounds in which the area
must lie for these four values of π and this radius.   [E]

5 The length of each side of a regular hexagon is 12.6 cm correct
to 3 significant figures. Calculate the **least** length that the
perimeter of the hexagon could be.   [E]

6 **After measuring the length and width of a rectangular piece of
card, Perveen draws and cuts out a smaller rectangle as shown in
the diagram.**

All the measurements are to the nearest cm.

Find:
   (a) the least possible area of card left.
   (b) the greatest possible area of card left.   [E]

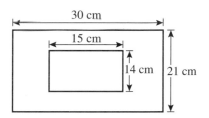

7 **Correct to 3 decimal places, $a = 2.236$.**
   (a) For this value of a, write down:
      (i) the upper bound,
      (ii) the lower bound.
Correct to 3 decimal places, $b = 1.414$.
   (b) Calculate:
      (i) the upper bound for the value of $a + b$.
      (ii) the lower bound for the value of $a + b$.
Write down all the figures on your calculator display for parts
(c) and (d) of this question.
   (c) Calculate the lower bound for the value ab.
   (d) Calculate the upper bound for the value $\dfrac{a}{b}$.   [E]

8 $y = \dfrac{x + 50}{x}$

$x = 30$, correct to one significant figure.

Work out:
   (a) the upper bound for y
   (b) the lower bound for y.

Test yourself	What to review

If your answer is incorrect, review in the Higher book:

1 The length of a rectangle is 135 cm and the width is 85 cm measured to the nearest cm.

(a) Calculate the least upper bound of the width.

Unit 23, Section 23.7
Unit 23, Section 23.5

(b) Calculate the greatest lower bound of the width.

Unit 23, Section 23.7
Unit 23, Section 23.5

(c) Calculate the greatest lower bound of the area.

Unit 23, Example 13
Unit 23, Example 10

(d) Give the area of the rectangle to a suitable accuracy.

Unit 23, Examples 20, 21 and 22
Unit 23, Examples 13, 14 and 15

Answers to Test yourself

1 (a) 85.5 cm   (b) 84.5 cm   (c) 11 365.25 cm^2 (d) 10 000 cm^2 to 1 significant figure

5 Solving equations

Sometimes you will need to solve linear equations, simultaneous equations and equations using graphical methods.

Key points to remember

1 To rearrange an equation you can:
- add the same quantity to both sides
- subtract the same quantity from both sides
- multiply both sides by the same quantity
- divide both sides by the same quantity
- take the square root of both sides

2 Whatever you do to one side of an equation you must do to the other side.

3 Simultaneous equations can bc solved:
- graphically, by drawing the straight lines of the two equations and finding the coordinates of the point of intersection.
- algebraically, using elimination or substitution.

4 You can use graphs to solve quadratic and cubic equations.

5 You can use a trial and improvement method to solve an equation by trying a value in the equation and changing it to bring the result closer and closer to the correct figure.

Example 1
Solve the equation:

$$3x - 1 = 4(5 - x)$$

Answer
Using **1** and **2**

$$3x - 1 = 4(5 - x)$$

multiply out the bracket $\quad 3x - 1 = 20 - 4x$
add 1 to both sides $\quad\quad\quad 3x = 21 - 4x$
add $4x$ to both sides $\quad\quad\; 7x = 21$
divide both sides by 7 $\quad\quad\; x = 3$ ———————————— Remember to check your answer:
$\text{LHS} = 3 \times 3 - 1 = 8$
$\text{RHS} = 4 \times (5 - 3) = 8$
$\text{LHS} = \text{RHS}$ so $x = 3$ is correct

Example 2

Solve $\quad \dfrac{3x}{2x - 4} = 13.5$

Answer

$$\frac{3x}{2x-4} = 13.5$$

Using **1** and **2**

multiply both sides by $(2x-4)$	$3x = 13.5(2x-4)$
expand bracket	$3x = 27x - 54$
subtract $27x$ from both sides	$3x - 27x = -54$
	$-24x = -54$
divide both sides by -24	$x = 2.25$

Worked examination question 1 [E]

Solve the simultaneous equations

$$3y = 2x - 5$$
$$y = x - 4$$

Answer

Using **3**

Method 1 Graphically

Choose 3 values for x and work out the values of y for each equation.

x	0	2	4
$y = x - 4$	-4	-2	0

x	1	4	7
$3y = 2x - 5$	-3	3	9
y	-1	1	3

Plot these two straight lines on a grid. The solution is where the two lines intercept, so $x = 7$, $y = 3$

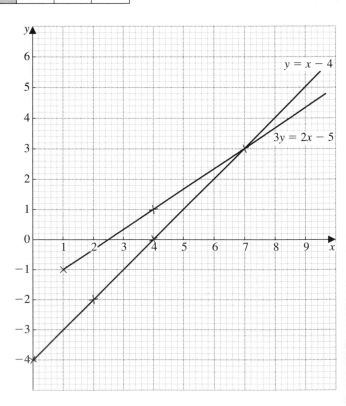

Method 2 Elimination
$$3y = 2x - 5 \quad (1)$$
$$y = x - 4 \quad (2)$$

Do $(1) - 2 \times (2)$ to eliminate x

$$3y = 2x - 5$$
Subtract $\quad 2y = 2x - 8$
$$y = 0 + 3$$
$$y = 3$$

Substitute this value into (2) to find x
$$3 = x - 4$$
add 4 to both sides $\quad 7 - x$
So $\quad x = 7$ and $y = 3$

Whichever method you use, remember to check your answer. In equation (1), $3y = 2x - 5$, LHS $= 3 \times 3 = 9$ RHS $= 2 \times 7 - 5 = 9$ LHS $=$ RHS so our answer is correct. To be absolutely sure, check the values work for the other equation too!

Method 3 Substitution
$$3y = 2x - 5 \quad (1)$$
$$y = x - 4 \quad (2)$$

From (2) $\quad y = x - 4$

Substitute $y = x - 4$ into (1)

$$3(x - 4) = 2x - 5$$
multiply brackets $\quad 3x - 12 = 2x - 5$
$+ 12$ both sides $\quad 3x = 2x + 7$
$- 2x$ both sides $\quad x = 7$

Substitute $x = 7$ into (2) $\quad y = 7 - 4$
$$y = 3$$
So $\quad x = 7$ and $y = 3$

Worked examination question 2 [E]

$$y = x^3 - 4x - 1$$

(a) Copy and complete the table of values.

x	-2	-1	0	1	2	3
y		2				

(b) On a grid, draw the graph of $y = x^3 - 4x - 1$ where $-2 \leqslant x \leqslant 5$ and $-5 \leqslant y \leqslant 15$

(c) By drawing a suitable straight line on the grid, solve the equation
$$x^3 - 4x - 3 = -2$$

(d) Using the method of trial and improvement, solve the equation
$$x^3 - 4x - 1 = 30$$
correct to one decimal place. You must show your working.

Answer

(a)

x	-2	-1	0	1	2	3
y	-1	2	-1	-4	-1	14

(b)

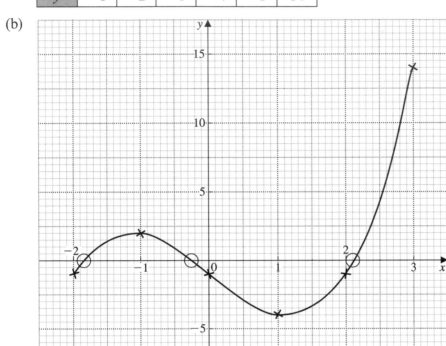

(c) Using **4**

Given $y = x^3 - 4x - 1$ (1)

Solve $x^3 - 4x - 3 = -2$ (2)

To make LHS of (2) the same as RHS of (1), add 2 to both sides of (2)

$$x^3 - 4x - 1 = 0$$

Then compare to equation (1)

So $y = 0$

Draw the straight line $y = 0$ and read off the values where this line intercepts the graph.

This gives $x = -1.85, -0.25,$ or 2.1

Note that the line $y = 0$ is the same line as the x-axis.

(d) Using **5**

$$x^3 - 4x - 1 = 30$$

when $x = 3$ $x^3 - 4x - 1 = 14$

when $x = 4$ $x^3 - 4x - 1 = 47$

Therefore solution lies between $x = 3$ and $x = 4$

try $x = 3.5$	$y = 27.86$	**too small**
try $x = 3.7$	$y = 34.85$	**too big**
try $x = 3.6$	$y = 31.26$	**too big**
try $x = 3.55$	$y = 29.54$	**too small**

Solution is $x = 3.6$ (to 1 d.p.)

Revision exercise 5

1 Solve the following equations:
   (a) $5x - 4 = 3x + 8$
   (b) $\frac{1}{2}(4 - 8x) = 5 - 3x$

   (c) $3(4x - 5) = 7(x + 3)$
   (d) $\frac{3}{x} + \frac{4}{5} = 5$

   (e) $\frac{35}{3x - 1} = 7$
   (f) $\frac{4x}{5x - 3} = 3$

   (g) $3(3x + 1) = 2(9 - 2x)$
   (h) $\frac{3x - 4}{2x + 1} = 2$

2 Solve the simultaneous equations:
   (a) $2p - 3q = 7$
       $p + q = 1$
   (b) $3x + 2y = 11$
       $x - y = 7$
   (c) $4p - q = 15$
       $2p - q = 9$
   (d) $3x + 2y = 8$
       $4x - 3y = 22$ [E]

3 (a) Draw the graph of $y = x^2 - 2x - 2$ and the graph of
      $y = x - 2$ on the same grid, where $-3 \leqslant x \leqslant 3$ and
      $-6 \leqslant y \leqslant 15$
   (b) Use the graphs to solve the equation $x^2 - 2x - 2 = x - 2$

4 (a) Draw the graph of $y = x^3 - x^2 - 4x + 2$ for values of x
      such that $-3 \leqslant x \leqslant 3$.

   The graph of $y = x^3 - x^2 - 4x + 2$ and the graph of $y = mx + c$,
   where m and c are constant, may be used to solve the equation
   $$x^3 - x^2 - 6x + 2 = 0$$
   (b) Find the values of m and c.
   (c) Using the values of m and c found in (b), draw the graph of
      $y = mx + c$ on the grid from (a).
   (d) Use the graph to solve the equation
   $$x^3 - x^2 - 6x + 2 = 0$$
      Give your answers correct to 1 decimal place.   [E]

5 (a) Draw the graph of $y = x^3 - 4x + 1$ for values of x such that
      $-2 \leqslant x \leqslant 2$
   (b) Use the graph to find approximate solutions in the range
      $-2 \leqslant x \leqslant 2$ of
      $$x^3 - 4x + 1 = 0$$
   (c) By drawing suitable straight lines on the grid, find
      approximate solutions in the range $-2 \leqslant x \leqslant 2$ of the
      equations:
      (i) $x^3 - 4x - 1 = 0$ (ii) $x^3 - 5x + 3 = 0$ [E]

6 Draw the graphs of $y = x^3$ and $y = 4 - x^2$ for values of x such
   that $-3 \leqslant x \leqslant 3$.
   Use the graphs to find a solution of $x^3 + x^2 - 4 = 0$, correct to
   1 decimal place.   [E]

7 Use the method of trial and improvement to solve the equation
$$x^3 - 4x = 61$$
Give your answer to 1 decimal place.

8 Use the method of trial and improvement to find the positive solution of
$$x^3 + x = 17.$$
Give your answer to 1 decimal place. [E]

Test yourself	What to review
	If your answer is incorrect, review in the Higher book:
1 Solve the equation $$3(2x - 1) = 7(x + 3)$$	*Unit 2, Examples 2 and 3* Unit 2, Examples 2 and 3
2 Solve the simultaneous equations $$3x + 4y = 8$$ $$2y + x = 2$$	*Unit 7, Example 10* Unit 7. Examples 9 and 10
3 (a) Draw the graph of $y = 2x^2 - 7x + 6$ **(b)** Use the graph to find approximate solutions to the equation $$2x^2 - 7x + 6 = 4$$	*Unit 18, page 374, Worked examination question* Unit 18, page 374, Worked examination question

Answers to Test yourself

1 $x = -24$ **2** $x = 4, y = -1$ **3 (a)**

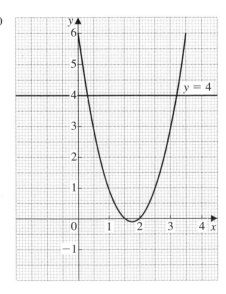

(b) $x = 0.3$ or $x = 3.2$

6 Quadratic equations

Quadratic equations can be used to represent a wide variety of situations. Quadratic equations take the form

$$ax^2 + bx + c = 0, \text{ where } a \neq 0$$

Key points to remember

1 The quadratic equation $ax^2 + bx + c = 0$, with $a \neq 0$ has two solutions (or roots) which may be equal.

2 Quadratic equations may be solved by factorization.

3 Quadratic equations may be solved by completing the square.
This rule may help:
$$x^2 + bx = (x + \tfrac{b}{2})^2 - (\tfrac{b}{2})^2$$

4 Quadratic equations may be solved by using the formula:
$$x = \frac{-b \pm \sqrt{b^2 - 4ac}}{2a}$$

5 If $\sqrt{b^2 - 4ac}$ is an integer then $ax^2 + bx + c$ can be factorized.
If $b^2 - 4ac$ is negative there are no real solutions.

6 Quadratic equations may be solved by a graphical method.

There is more on factorizing quadratics in Unit 1.

Worked examination question 1 [E]

Solve $\qquad x^2 - 5x - 14 = 0$

Answer

Using **5**
$$\sqrt{b^2 - 4ac} = \sqrt{(-5^2) - 4(1)(-14)} = \sqrt{25 + 56} = \sqrt{81} = 9$$
Hence $x^2 - 5x - 14$ can be factorized.

$$x^2 - 5x - 14 = 0$$

Using **2** $\qquad\qquad (x + 2)(x - 7) = 0$
Then either $\qquad (x + 2) = 0 \quad$ or $\ (x - 7) = 0$
So $\qquad\qquad\qquad x = -2 \ $ or $\qquad\quad x = 7$

Look for two numbers that multiply to −14 and add to −5.

Worked examination question 2 [E]

A rectangular carpet is placed centrally on the floor of a room 6 metres by 4 metres. The distance from the edges of the carpet to the walls is x metres. The carpet covers half the area of the floor.
(a) Show that $x^2 - 5x + 3 = 0$
(b) Solve the equation in (a) to find x, correct to 3 significant figures.

Answer

(a) Width of carpet $= 4 - 2x$
Length of carpet $= 6 - 2x$
Area of carpet $= \frac{1}{2} \times 6 \times 4 = 12$
Area of carpet $= 12 =$ width $\times$ length $= (4 - 2x)(6 - 2x)$
$$12 = 24 - 8x - 12x + 4x^2$$
$$12 = 4x^2 - 20x + 24$$

divide by 4 $4x^2 - 20x + 12 = 0$
$$x^2 - 5x + 3 = 0$$

(b) Using method of completing the square:
$$x^2 - 5x = -3$$
Using **3** $(x - \frac{5}{2})^2 - \frac{25}{4} = -3$
$$(x - \frac{5}{2})^2 = -3 + \frac{25}{4}$$

Square root both sides $x - \frac{5}{2} = \pm\sqrt{\frac{13}{4}}$

Add $\frac{5}{2}$ to both sides $x = \frac{5}{2} \pm \sqrt{\frac{13}{4}}$
So $x = 2.5 \pm 1.803$
$$x = 0.697$$
correct to 3 significant figures

> When a question asks you to show the answer to a number of decimal places or significant figures, use either completing the square or the formula method.

Or use the formula with $a = 1$, $b = -5$ and $c = 3$

$x = 4.30$ is not a solution as the width is only 4 metres

Worked examination question 3 [E]

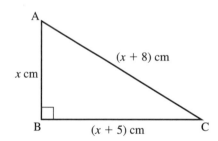

ABC is a triangle with angle $ABC = 90°$.
$AB = x \,\text{cm}$
$BC = (x + 5) \,\text{cm}$
$AC = (x + 8) \,\text{cm}$

(a) Prove that
$$x^2 - 6x - 39 = 0$$

(b) Solve this equation for x, leaving your answer in the most simplified surd form.

Answer

(a) $AB^2 + BC^2 = AC^2$ By Pythagoras
so $AB^2 = AC^2 - BC^2$
$$AB^2 = (AC - BC)(AC + BC)$$ Difference of 2 squares

so
$$x^2 = 3(2x + 13)$$

i.e. $x^2 = 6x + 39$

so $x^2 - 6x - 39 = 0$

(b) To solve, by completing the square:

$$(x - 3)^2 - 9 - 39 = 0$$
$$(x - 3)^2 = 48$$
$$x - 3 = \pm\sqrt{48}$$
$$x - 3 = \pm\sqrt{3 \times 16}$$
$$x - 3 = \pm 4\sqrt{3}$$

but since $x > 0$ (side of triangle)

$$x = 3 + 4\sqrt{3}\,\text{cm}.$$

Example 1

Solve the quadratic equation $2x^2 + 5x - 6 = 0$ correct to 2 decimal places.

Answer

Using **4** $\quad x = \dfrac{-b \pm \sqrt{b^2 - 4ac}}{2a}$ where $a = 2$, $b = 5$, $c = -6$

Substitute these values into the rule

$$x = \frac{-5 \pm \sqrt{5^2 - 4(2)(-6)}}{2 \times 2}$$

$$= \frac{-5 \pm \sqrt{25 + 48}}{4}$$

$$= \frac{-5 \pm \sqrt{73}}{4}$$

$$x = 0.89 \text{ or } x = -3.39 \text{ correct to 2 d.p.}$$

Revision exercise 6

1 Solve these equations:
   (a) $x^2 - 5 = 0$ (b) $x^2 - 7x = 0$
   (c) $x^2 + 7x + 12 = 0$ (d) $x^2 - 3x - 18 = 0$
   (e) $x^2 + 10x + 24 = 0$ (f) $x^2 - 6x - 16 = 0$
   (g) $2x^2 - 5x - 3 = 0$ (h) $5x^2 - 23x - 10 = 0$
   (i) $6x^2 + 7x - 5 = 0$

2 Solve the following equations using both completing the square and formula methods. Give your answers
   (i) in surd form and
   (ii) correct to 2 decimal places.

    (a) $x^2 - 7x = 3$ **(b)** $3x^2 - 4x = 2$ **(c)** $x^2 - 3x - 1 = 0$
    (d) $2x^2 + 3x - 4 = 0$ **(e)** $3x^2 - 7x + 1 = 0$

3 **(a)** Draw the graph of $f(x) = 4 - x^2$ for $-3 \leqslant x \leqslant 3$
   (b) By drawing a suitable line on the graph find approximate
      solutions to the equation $4 - x^2 = x$ [E]

4 Fred cycled from home to his friend's house and back again.
   The distance from Fred's home to his friend's house is 20 km.
   On his way from home to his friend's house, Fred cycled at
   x km per hour.
   On his way back, Fred's speed had decreased by 2 km per hour.
   It took Fred 4 hours altogether to cycle to his friend's house
   and back.
   (a) Write down an equation for x.
   (b) Show that the equation can be written as
$$x^2 - 12x + 10 = 0$$
   (c) Solve the equation in part **(b)**.
      Give your answer in surd form.

   Only one of the answers in part **(c)** can be Fred's speed.
   (d) Explain why.   [E]

5 Rob, taking part in a sponsored walk, walked from Merlow to
   Fircombe, a distance of 12 km, and then he walked back from
   Fircombe to Merlow.
   Rob's speed on the outward journey was x km/h.
   On the return journey he was tired and he walked 2 km/h
   slower than on the outward journey.
   (a) Write down, in terms of x, the time taken for the whole
      journey.

   Rob was walking for a total of $3\frac{1}{2}$ hours.
   (b) **(i)** Use your answer to part **(a)** to form an equation.
       (ii) Show that this equation can be written as
$$7x^2 - 62x + 48 = 0$$
   (c) Calculate Rob's speed on the outward journey.   [E]

Test yourself	**What to review**
	If your answer is incorrect, review in the Higher book:
1 Solve by factorizing the equation: $$2x^2 - 7x - 15 = 0$$	*Unit 21, Example 2* Unit 21, Example 2

2 Solve by completing the square:
$$x^2 + 5x - 1 = 0$$

Unit 21, Example 8
Unit 21, Example 8

3 Solve by the formula method:
$$3x^2 + 11x - 2 = 0$$

Unit 21, Example 9
Unit 21, Example 9

4 Use a graphical method to solve the equation:
$$x = x^2 + 2x - 3$$

Unit 21, Example 18 and 23
Unit 21, Example 23

Answers to Test yourself

1 $x = -\frac{3}{2}$ or $x = 5$ **2** $x = -5.19$ or $+0.19$ **3** $x = 0.17$ or -3.84 **4** $x = 1.30$ or -2.30
      or $-\frac{5}{2} \pm \frac{1}{2}\sqrt{29}$

7 Inequalities

Inequalities are similar to equations and formulae and similar procedures can be applied to solve or represent them.

Key points to remember

1 To solve a linear inequality you can

- add the same quantity to *both* sides
- subtract the same quantity from *both* sides
- multiply or divide *both* sides by a *positive* quantity
- multiply or divide *both* sides by a *negative* quantity and *change* the inequality sign to its opposite.

For example, $2 < 5$ implies $-2 > -5$

Remember these inequality signs
$\geqslant$ greater than or equal to
$>$ greater than
$\leqslant$ less than or equal to
$<$ less than

2 To solve a quadratic inequality:

- replace the equality sign by $=$ and solve the quadratic equation to give two critical values
- pick a value of x between the two critical values and use it to test the inequality to see whether the solutions lie between the two critical values, or in the other two regions not between the two critical values.

Worked examination question 1 [E]

Solve the inequality
$$2x + 5 < 8$$

Answer

$$2x + 5 < 8$$
Using **1**
Subtract 5 from both sides $\qquad 2x < 3$
Divide both sides by 2 $\qquad x < \frac{3}{2}$

Worked examination question 2 [E]

(a) Draw the straight lines $x + y = 2$, $y = 6$ and $x + 2y = 2$ on a coordinate grid $-6 \leqslant x \leqslant 7$
(b) Shade in the region defined by the inequalities
$$y < 6$$
$$x + 2y > 2$$
$$x + y < 2$$

Answer

(a) Using **2** to draw the line $x + y = 2$, work out 3 coordinates

x	-6	0	7
y	8	2	-5

To draw the line $y = 6$ simply draw a horizontal line across at $y = 6$

To draw the line $x + 2y = 2$ work out 3 coordinates

x	-6	0	7
y	4	1	$-2\frac{1}{2}$

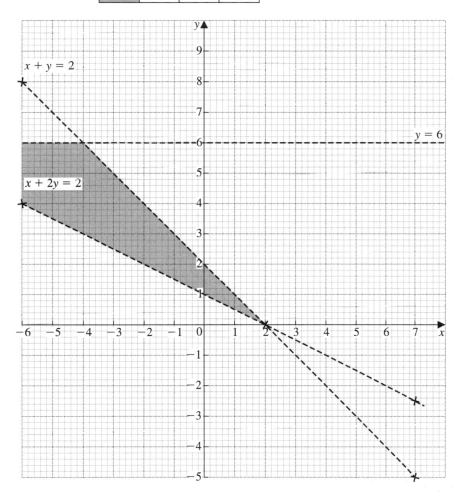

Because $y < 6$, the line $y = 6$ lies in the unwanted region, so it is drawn as a broken line. The other two lines are similarly drawn with broken lines.

(b) Using **2**
choose the region required to satisfy all the inequalities.

Test by substituting a point from within the coordinate grid, say $(-3, 3)$, putting this value in each inequality.

Checking: $\qquad y < 6, 3 < 6 \quad$ OK

$\qquad x + 2y > 2, -3 + 6 > 2 \quad$ OK

$\qquad x + y < 2, -3 + 3 < 2 \quad$ OK

So shade the region bounded by the lines $y = 6$, $x + 2y = 2$ and $x + y = 2$ that contains the point $(-3, 3)$.

Example 1
Solve the inequality
$$x^2 < 16$$

Answer

Using **2**
replace $<$ by $=$ $\quad\quad x^2 = 16$
square root both sides $\quad x = \pm 4$

Choose a value of x between $+4$ and -4 say 0, then $0^2 < 9$ is true,
so x lies in the region between -4 and $+4$, written as $-4 < x < 4$

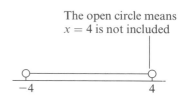

The open circle means
$x = 4$ is not included

Example 2
Solve the inequality
$$(x - 3)^2 \leqslant 36$$

Answer

Using **2**
replace $\leqslant$ with $=$ $\quad\quad (x - 3)^2 = 36$
square root both sides $\quad\quad x - 3 = \pm 6$
add 3 to both sides $\quad\quad\quad x = +9 \text{ or } -3$

Choose a value between 9 and -3, say 0
then $\quad\quad (0 - 3)^2 = 9 \leqslant 36$ is true
So x lies in the region $+9$ to -3, written as $-3 \leqslant x \leqslant 9$

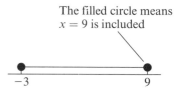

The filled circle means
$x = 9$ is included

Revision exercise 7

1 Solve these inequalities:
   (a) $2x + 3 \geqslant 7$
   (b) $3x + 2 \geqslant 6x + 1$
   (c) $-2x \geqslant -9$
   (d) $6 - 3x \geqslant 4x$
   (e) $4 + 5x \geqslant 4x - 2$
   (f) $4x - 7 \leqslant 8 - x$
   (g) $9 - 2x \leqslant 11 - 5x$
   (h) $13 - 10x > 5x - 12$

2 Draw the straight lines $y = x$, $y = x + 2$ and $y = -2x + 3$ on a coordinate grid.

   Shade in the region on your coordinate grid defined by the inequalities $y > x$, $y < x + 2$, $y \leqslant -2x + 3$

3 Shade in the region on a coordinate grid defined by $y < 2x$, $y < 4x + 9$, $x > -2$

4 Solve these inequalities:
   (a) $x^2 < 36$
   (b) $x^2 > 81$
   (c) $9x^2 < 64$

   (d) $(x + 1)^2 \geqslant 49$
   (e) $(3 - x)^2 < 25$
   (f) $\dfrac{(3x - 1)^2}{4} < 9$

5 **(a)** Solve the inequality

$$4x + 6 \leqslant 13$$

A sketch of the graph of $y = 4x + 6$ is shown below.

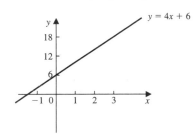

(b) Copy the graph.
By first sketching the graphs of two further lines, shade in the region given by the three inequalities

$$x \geqslant 3 \qquad y \geqslant 13 \quad \text{and} \quad y \leqslant 4x + 6$$

[E]

Test yourself	What to review
	If your answer is incorrect, review in the Higher book:
1 Solve $\qquad 3x - 7 \geqslant 2x + 8$	*Unit 2, Examples 8 and 9* Unit 2, Examples 8 and 9
2 Shade the region satisfied by $y < 5$, $x > -4$ and $y > 2x + 5$	*Unit 7, Section 7.6* Unit 7, Section 7.7
3 Solve $\qquad (5 - x)^2 > 100$	*Unit 21, Example 16* Unit 21, Example 21

Answers to Test yourself

1 $x \geqslant 15$ **2** **3** $-5 > x$ or $x > 15$

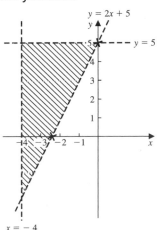

8 Proportion

Key points to remember

1 $y \propto x$ means y is directly proportional to x.

2 When a graph connecting two quantities is a straight line through the origin then one quantity is directly proportional to the other.

3 When y is directly proportional to x:
- $y \propto x$ is the proportionality statement
- $y = kx$ is the proportionality formula, where k is the constant of proportionality.

4 When y is directly proportional to the square of x:
- $y \propto x^2$ is the proportionality statement
- $y = kx^2$ is the proportionality formula, where k is the constant of proportionality.

5 When y is directly proportional to the cube of x:
- $y \propto x^3$ is the proportionality statement
- $y = kx^3$ is the proportionality formula, where k is the constant of proportionality.

6 When y is inversely proportional to x:
- $y \propto \dfrac{1}{x}$ is the proportionality statement

- $y = \dfrac{k}{x}$ is the proportionality formula, where k is the constant of proportionality.

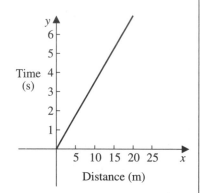

In the graph distance is proportional to time.

Note: the constant of proportionality is often called the constant of variation.

Worked examination question 1 [E]

A ball is dropped to the floor from a height of h centimetres. It bounces to a height of y centimetres.
y is directly proportional to h.
(a) Sketch a graph to show the relationship between y and h.
    When $h = 120$, $y = 80$
(b) Find y when $h = 150$

Answer
(a) Using **2**

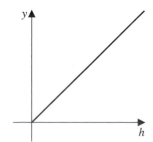

(b) Using **3**
$$y = kh$$
When $h = 120$, $y = 80$
Substitute these values in the formula
$$80 = k120$$
$$\therefore \quad k = \frac{80}{120} = \frac{2}{3}$$
$\therefore$ formula is $\quad y = \frac{2}{3}h$

So when $\quad h = 150$
$$y = \frac{2}{3} \times 150$$
$$y = 100 \, \text{cm}$$

Worked examination question 2 [E]

When a stone is thrown upwards with initial speed s metres per second, it reaches a maximum height h metres.

Given that h varies directly as the square of s and that $h = 5$ when $s = 10$

Note: 'h varies directly as the square of s' means h is directly proportional to the square of s.

(a) Work out a formula connecting h and s.
(b) Calculate the value of s when $h = 20$.
(c) Two stones are thrown up. The ratio of their speeds is $3:1$. Work out the ratio of maximum heights achieved.

Answer

(a) Using **4** $\qquad h = ks^2$
Given $h = 5$ when $s = 10$
$$5 = k \times 10^2$$
$$5 = 100k$$
$$k = \frac{5}{100} = \frac{1}{20}$$
$\therefore$ formula is $\qquad h = \frac{1}{20}s^2$

(b) When $h = 20$
$$20 = \frac{1}{20} \times s^2$$
$$20 \times 20 = s^2$$
$$s^2 = 400$$
$$s = 20 \, \text{metres}$$

(c) We know $h = \frac{1}{20}s^2$

When speed is $3s$ $\qquad h = \frac{1}{20} \times (3s)^2 = \frac{9}{20}s^2$

When speed is $1s$ $\qquad h = \frac{1}{20} \times (1s)^2 = \frac{1}{20}s^2$

$\therefore$ ratio of heights is $\frac{9}{20} : \frac{1}{20} = 9:1$

Revision exercise 8

1 The cost of toothpaste in a tube is directly proportional to the amount of toothpaste in the tube.
A 100 ml tube costs £1.40.
   (a) Find a rule connecting the cost of the toothpaste and amount of toothpaste.
   (b) Find the cost of a tube containing
   (i) 50 ml   **(ii)** 70 ml   **(iii)** 135 ml   **(iv)** 220 ml
   (c) A tube of toothpaste costs £1.75.
   How much toothpaste is in the tube?

2 The distance (d metres) travelled by a stone falling vertically varies in direct proportion to the square of the time (t seconds) for which it falls.
   (a) Write a formula to connect d, t and the constant of variation k.

A stone takes 2 seconds to fall 20 metres.
   (b) Find the value of k.
   (c) How far will the stone fall in 4 seconds?

A stone is dropped from a balloon which is 500 metres above the ground.
   (d) How many seconds will the stone take to reach the ground?

[E]

3 f is inversely proportional to w.
   (a) Find a rule connecting f and w and the constant of variation k.
   (b) When $w = 2, f = 1600$.
   Find the value of k.
   (c) Find f when   **(i)** $w = 5$ **(ii)** $w = 0.2$
   (d) $f = 5000$, find w.

4 There are two similar saucepans in a kitchen. The smaller one holds 1.5 litres and is 12 cm tall.
The larger saucepan is 16.4 cm tall.
How much will the larger saucepan hold when full?

5 a varies in direct proportion to the cube of b.
   (a) Write down a formula to connect a and b and the constant of variation, k.
   (b) Given $a = 128$ when $b = 4$, find k.
   (c) Find a when $b = 6$.
   (d) Find b when $a = 686$.

6 p is directly proportional to q^2.
When $p = 80, q = -4$.
   (a) Work out the value of p when $q = 10$.
   (b) Work out the value of q when $p = 180$.

7 When a car travels at a speed of s m.p.h., its braking distance, b feet, is directly proportional to s^2.
When $s = 20$ mph, b and s are numerically equal.
Calculate the braking distance for a car travelling at 60 mph.

8 The time, t minutes, taken for a satellite to orbit the Earth is inversely proportional to the speed, V kilometres per minute, of the satellite.
(a) Write a formula relating t, V and k, the constant of proportion.

The satellite orbits the Earth every 100 minutes travelling at a speed of 400 kilometres per minute.
(b) Calculate the value of k.   [E]

Test yourself	**What to review**
	If your answer is incorrect, review in the Higher book:
1 a is directly proportional to b. When $a = 48$, $b = 30$ **(a)** Work out the rule connecting a and b. **(b)** Work out b when $a = 41$	*Unit 17, Example 4* Unit 17, Example 4
2 s is directly proportional to the square of t. When $s = 5$, $t = 2$ **(a)** Work out the rule connecting s and t. **(b)** Work out t when $s = 425$	*Unit 17, Section 17.6* Unit 17, Section 17.6
3 x is inversely proportional to the square of y. When $x = 20$, $y = 2$ **(a)** Work out the rule connecting x and y. **(b)** Find y when $x = 160$	*Unit 17, Example 7* Unit 17, Example 7

Answers to Test yourself

1 **(a)** $a = 1.6b$ **(b)** 25.625 **2** **(a)** $s = \frac{5}{4}t^2$ **(b)** $t = 18.4$ (to 1 d.p.)   **3** **(a)** $x = \frac{80}{y^2}$ **(b)** $y = \pm 0.707$ (to 3 d.p.)

9 Applying transformations to sketch graphs

Key points to remember

1 A function is a rule which changes one number into another number.

For example,

if $\quad\quad\quad f(x) = 3x^2 - 4$

then $\quad\quad\quad f(2) = 3 \times (2)^2 - 4$

$\quad\quad\quad\quad\quad\quad = 3 \times 4 - 4$

$\quad\quad\quad\quad\quad\quad = 12 - 4 = 8$

2 The graph of $y = x^2 + a$ is the graph of $y = x^2$ translated a units vertically

- in the positive y-direction if $a > 0$
- in the negative y-direction if $a < 0$

In the diagram opposite, the graph of $y = x^2 + 2$ is the graph of $y = x^2 - 3$ translated by 5 units vertically in the positive y-direction

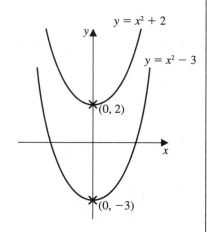

3 The graph of $y = x + a$ is the graph of $y = x$ translated a units vertically

- in the positive direction if $a > 0$
- in the negative direction if $a < 0$

In the diagram, the graph $y = x + 9$ is the graph of $y = x$ translated 9 units vertically in the positive y-direction

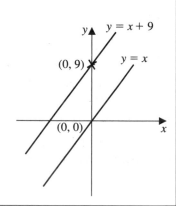

4   For any function f, the graph of $y = f(x) + a$ is the graph of $y = f(x)$ translated a units vertically
- in the positive direction if $a > 0$
- in the negative direction if $a < 0$

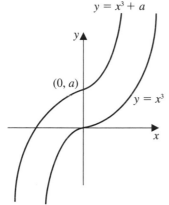

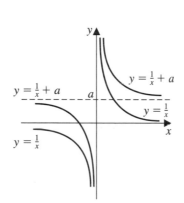

$y = x^3 + a$ is a translation of $y = x^3$ $y = \frac{1}{x} + a$ is a translation of $y = \frac{1}{x}$

5   The graph of $y = (x + a)^2$ is the graph of $y = x^2$ translated a units horizontally
- in the *negative x*-direction if $a > 0$
- in the *positive x*-direction if $a < 0$

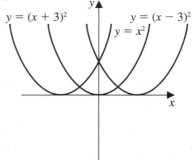

6   The graph of $y = f(x + a)$ is the graph of $y = f(x)$ translated a units horizontally
- in the *negative x*-direction if $a > 0$
- in the *positive x*-direction if $a < 0$

7   The graph of $y = f(x + a) + b$ is the graph of $y = f(x)$ translated a units horizontally
- in the *negative x*-direction if $a > 0$
- in the *positive x*-direction if $a < 0$

followed by a translation of b units vertically
- upwards if $b > 0$
- downwards if $b < 0$

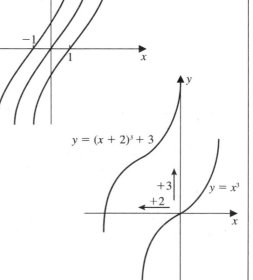

8 For any function f, the graph $y = -f(x)$ is obtained by reflecting $y = f(x)$ in the x-axis.

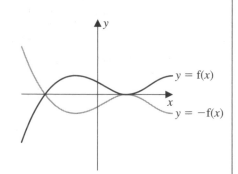

9 For any function f, the graph $y = f(-x)$ is obtained by reflecting $y = f(x)$ in the y-axis.

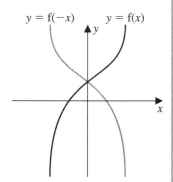

10 For any function f, the graph of $y = af(x)$, where a is a positive constant, is obtained from $y = f(x)$ by applying a stretch of scale factor a parallel to the y-axis.
(Note: the larger the value of a, the steeper the curve.)

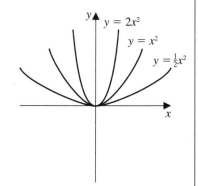

11 For any function f, the graph of $y = f(ax)$, where a is a positive constant, is obtained from $y = f(x)$ by applying a stretch of scale factor $\dfrac{1}{a}$ parallel to the x-axis.
(Note: the larger the value of a, the steeper the curve.)

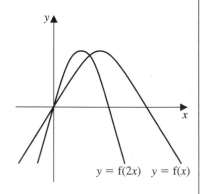

Worked examination question 1 [E]

This is a sketch of $y = f(x)$, where

$$f(x) = (x + 3)(x - 2)(x - 4)$$

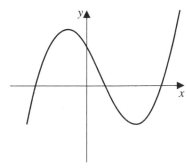

(a) Calculate the value of $f(0)$.
(b) Copy the sketch graph and on the same diagram, sketch the graph of $y = f(-x)$.
(c) Describe fully the single geometric transformation which maps the graph of $y = f(x)$ onto the graph of $y = f(-x)$.

The equation $f(x) = f(-x)$ has a solution $x = 0$.
It also has a positive solution x such that

$$n < x < n + 1$$

where n is a positive integer.

(d) Write down the value of n.

Answer

(a) Using **1**

$$f(0) = (0 + 3)(0 - 2)(0 - 4)$$
$$= 3 \times -2 \times -4$$
$$= 24$$

(b) Using **9**

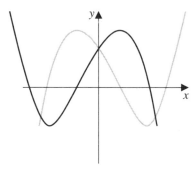

(c) Using **9** reflection in the y-axis.

(d) When $f(x) = 0$

$$x = -3 \text{ or } x = 2 \text{ or } x = 4$$

$$f(-x) = (-x + 3)(-x - 2)(-x - 4)$$

To find $f(-x)$, substitute $-x$ for x in $f(x)$.

This crosses the x-axis when $f(-x) = 0$, which is when

$$-x + 3 = 0 \text{ or } -x - 2 = 0 \quad \text{or } -x - 4 = 0$$
$$x = 3 \text{ or } \qquad x = -2 \text{ or } \qquad x = -4$$

The positive solution is where the two graphs intersect.
From the graph this value lies between $x = 3$ and $x = 4$.
So $n = 3$.

Worked examination question 2 [E]

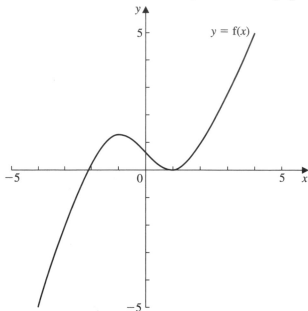

The graph of $y = f(x)$ has been drawn on the diagram.
Copy the diagram above and sketch the graph of $y = f(x - 2)$.

Answer

Using **6**

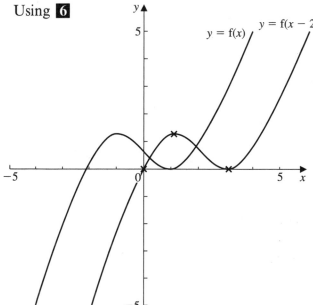

Revision exercise 9

1 $f(x) = 5x^2 - 3$

Find **(a)** $f(0)$ **(b)** $f(1)$ **(c)** $f(-2)$ **(d)** $f(5)$

2 A graph of $y = f(x)$ has been drawn on the grid below.

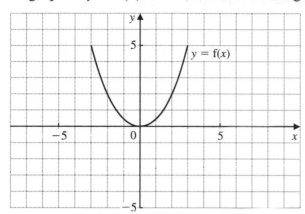

(a) Copy the graph and sketch the graph of $y = f(x) - 4$.

(b) On the same grid sketch the graph of $y = f(x - 4)$.   [E]

3 The graph of $y = f(x)$, where $f(x) = 4 - x^2$ is drawn opposite for $-3 \leqslant x \leqslant 3$.

(a) Explain how you would use the graph of $y = f(x)$ to draw the graph

   (i) $y = f(x) - 1$

   (ii) $y = f(x + 1)$

   Sketch the graphs in (i) and (ii).

(b) Sketch the graph of $y = -f(x)$.

   Your graph should include the coordinates of the points where the graph crosses the axes.   [E]

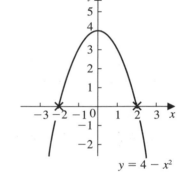

$y = 4 - x^2$

4 A sketch of the graph of $y = x^2$ is drawn opposite.

(a) Copy the graph and sketch a graph of $y = (x + 1)^2$.

The two graphs intersect at one point.

(b) Calculate the x-coordinate of the point of intersection.

Two points on the graph of $y = (x + 1)^2$ are at a distance of 9 units from the x-axis.

(c) Calculate the x-coordinates of these two points.   [E]

5 Sketch the graphs of $y = \dfrac{1}{x}$ and $y = \dfrac{1}{x} - 2$ on the same grid.

6 Sketch the graphs of $y = x^2$ and $y = (x + 1)^2 + 3$ on the same grid.

7 (a) Sketch the graph given by the function
$$f(x) = (x + 1)(x - 1)(x + 3)$$
on a grid.

(b) On the same grid sketch $-f(x)$.

(c) What transformation maps $f(x)$ on to $-f(x)$?

8 Sketch the graph of $y = 2\cos 3x$ for $-180° \leqslant x \leqslant 180°$.

There is more on trigonometric curves in Unit 15.

Test yourself	What to review
	If your answer is incorrect, review in the Higher book:
1 $f(x) = x^3 - 3$ Find $f(-4)$	*Unit 24, Example 1* Unit 24, Example 1
2 Sketch on the same grid $f(x) = x^3$ and $f(x) = x^3 - 3$	*Unit 24, Section 24.2* Unit 24, Section 24.2
3 The graph shows the function $y = f(x)$.	*Unit 24, Section 24.5* Unit 24, Section 24.5

(a) Sketch the graph of $y = f(-x)$
(b) What single transformation maps $f(x)$ onto $f(-x)$?

4 Sketch the graph of $y = 2 \sin 4x$ for $-180° \leqslant x \leqslant 180°$	*Unit 24, Section 24.7* Unit 24, Section 24.7

Answers to Test yourself

1 −67   **2**

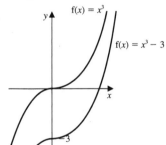

3 (a)

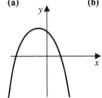

(b) Reflection in the y-axis.

4

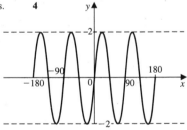

10 Straight line graphs, circles and solving advanced simultaneous equations

This chapter looks at the important features of straight line graphs, the equation of a circle and the solution of two equations, one of which is linear and the other quadratic.

Key points to remember

1 The equation of any straight line graph can be written as:

$$y = mx + c$$

The gradient of the line is m.
The line crosses the y axis at the point with coordinates $(0, c)$.

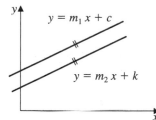

2 The two straight lines

$$y = m_1 x + c \quad \text{and}$$
$$y = m_2 x + k$$

will be **parallel** if their gradients are equal,
i.e. $m_1 = m_2$.

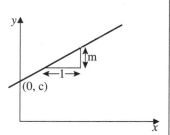

3 The two straight lines

$$y = m_1 x + c \quad \text{and} \quad y = m_2 x + k$$

will be **perpendicular** if

$$m_1 \times m_2 = -1 \quad or \quad m_2 = -\frac{1}{m}.$$

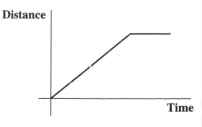

4 The gradient of a distance time graph is a measure of velocity.

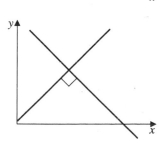

5 The gradient of a velocity time graph is a measure of acceleration.

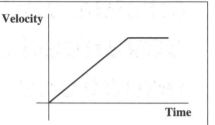

6 The area under a velocity time graph is a measure of the distance travelled.

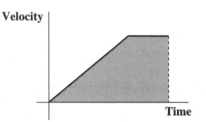

7 The equation of a circle centre the origin (0, 0) of radius r, i.e.:

$$x^2 + y^2 = r^2$$

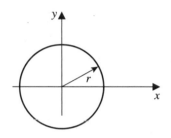

8 A straight line graph can intersect a circle on either:

2 points
1 point (a tangent)
or 0 points.

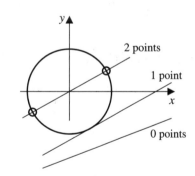

9 A straight line graph could meet a 'quadratic' other than a circle in either:

2 points
1 point (a tangent)
or 0 points.

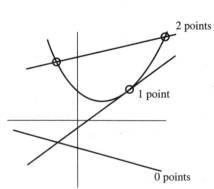

> **10** Solving two equations, one of which is linear (a straight line) and one of which is quadratic, could lead to:
>
> 2 solutions,   1 solution   or   0 solutions.

Example 1

The equation of a straight line, L, is

$$y = 3x - 2.$$

(a) A line, M, is parallel to L and passes through the point (0, 5). Work out the equation of the line M.

(b) A line, N, is perpendicular to L and passes through the point (12, 7). Work out the equation of N.

Answer

(a) The equation of line M will be

$$y = mx + c$$

Since M is parallel to L, its gradient = the gradient of L. So m = 3.

The intercept of M with the y axis is 5. so the equation of M is:

$$y = 3x + 5$$

(b) The equation of N is:

$$y = nx + k.$$

Since N is perpendicular to L

the gradient of N $= \dfrac{-1}{\text{gradient of L}}$

So the gradient of N is $\dfrac{-1}{3}$

So the equation of N is

$$y = \frac{-1}{3}x + k$$

But N passes through the point (12, 7) so, when $y = 7$, $x = 12$ i.e.

$$7 = \frac{-1}{3}(12) + k$$

i.e. $7 = -4 + k$

$k = 11$

So the equation of N is

$$y = -\frac{1}{3}x + 11.$$

Example 2

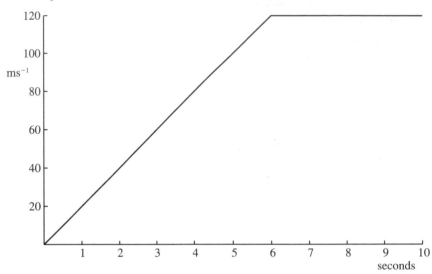

The diagram represents the velocity-timed graph for a racing car during the first 10 seconds of a test drive.

The car accelerates uniformly to a velocity of $120\,\text{ms}^{-1}$ in six seconds. It then continues at a constant velocity of $120\,\text{ms}^{-1}$.

(a) Work out the car's acceleration during the first six seconds.

(b) Work out the distances travelled by the car in the 10 seconds.

Answer

(a) The acceleration of the car is the gradient of the straight line during the first 6 seconds. This gradient is:

$$\frac{120\,\text{ms}^{-1}}{6\,\text{s}} = 20\,\text{ms}^{-2}$$

(b) The distance travelled is the area under the graph.

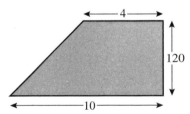

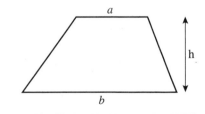

Using the formula for the area of a trapezium, this area is:

$$\tfrac{1}{2}(4 + 10) \times 120$$

$$= 7 \times 120$$

$$= 840 \text{ metres}$$

Note: you could split up the shape as below:

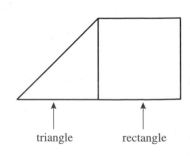

triangle   rectangle

Example 3

Work out the area bounded by:

    the positive x-axis,
    the positive y-axis,

at the curve with equation $x^2 + y^2 = 36$.
You may leave your answer in terms of π.

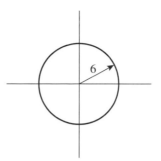

Answer

The curve $x^2 + y^2 = 36$ is a circle, centre $(0, 0)$, of radius 6 units.
So the area required is:

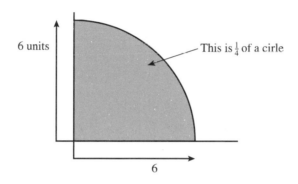

6 units

This is $\frac{1}{4}$ of a cirle

6

$$\text{Area} = \frac{\pi r^2}{4} = \frac{\pi \times 6^2}{4} = \frac{\pi \times 36}{4} = 9\pi \text{ sq units}$$

Example 4

Solve the equation:

$$x + y = 1$$
$$x^2 + y^2 = 16$$

Leave your answer in surd form.

Answer

Rearrange the first equation:

$$y = 1 - x$$

Substituting into the second equation gives:

$$x^2 + (1 - x)^2 = 16$$
$$x^2 + 1 - 2x + x^2 - 16$$

So $2x^2 - 2x - 15 = 0$ | Divide by 2 |

$$x^2 - x - \tfrac{15}{2} = 0$$

Complete the square:

$$\left(x - \tfrac{1}{2}\right)^2 - \tfrac{1}{4} - \tfrac{15}{2} = 0$$

$$\left(x - \tfrac{1}{2}\right)^2 = \tfrac{1}{4} + \tfrac{15}{2}$$

$$\left(x - \tfrac{1}{2}\right)^2 = \tfrac{31}{4}$$

$$x - \tfrac{1}{2} = \pm \tfrac{\sqrt{31}}{2}$$

$$x = \tfrac{1}{2} = \pm \tfrac{\sqrt{31}}{2}$$

Example 5

Solve the equation:

$$4x^2 - y^2 = 40$$
$$2x + y = 10$$

For the first two equations, using the differences between two squarcs gives:

$$(2x - y)(2x + y) = 40$$

but we know from the second equation that $2x + y = 10$ so $(2x - y)(2x + y) = 40$ becomes:

$$(2x - y) \times 10 = 40$$

i.e.

$$2x - y = 4$$

Now we have:

$$2x - y = 4$$
$$2x + y = 10$$

Adding gives:

$$4x = 14$$

so $x = 3\tfrac{1}{2}$

Substituting $x = 3\tfrac{1}{2}$ into $2x - y = 4$ gives:

$$2(3\tfrac{1}{2}) - y = 4$$
$$7 - y = 4$$

So $y = 3$.

Hence the solution is:

$$x = 3\tfrac{1}{2}, \quad y = 3.$$

> Note:
> You could also rearrange
> $$2x + y = 10$$
> to $$y = 10 - 2x$$
> and substitute into
> $$4x^2 - y^2 = 40$$
> to give
> $$4x^2 - (10 - 2x)^2 = 40$$
> $$4x^2 - (100 - 40x + 4x^2) = 40$$
> $$4x^2 - 100 + 40x - 4x^2 = 40$$
> i.e.
> $$-100 + 40x = 40$$
> $$40x = 140$$
> $$4x = 14$$
> $$x = 3\tfrac{1}{2}$$

Revision exercise 10

1 (a) The equation of a straight line is:

$$3x + 2y = 12$$

Work out the gradient of this straight line.

(b) The line meets the y-axis at the point $(0, c)$.
Work out the value of c.

(c) A second straight line is parallel to

$$3x + 2y = 12$$

It meets the y-axis at $(0, 7)$.
Work out the equation of the second straight line.

(d) A third straight line is perpendicular to

$$3x + 2y = 12$$

It passes through the point $(-6, 5)$.
Work out the equation of the third straight line.

2 (a) Draw the graph of $y = -\frac{1}{2}x + 7$

(b) A straight line is perpendicular to $y = -\frac{1}{2}x + 7$.

It passes through the points $(-2, 5)$.
Work out the equation of this straight line.

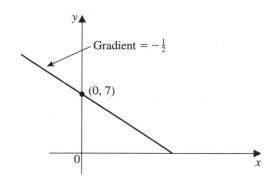

3 The diagram represents a velocity-time graph of a 30-second run made by Joe.

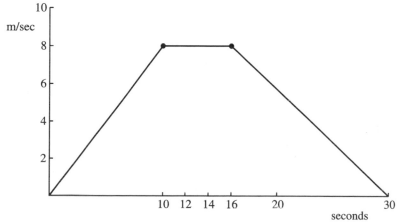

During the first ten seconds Joe accelerates uniformly to a velocity of $8 \, \text{m/sec}^{-1}$.

(a) Work out his acceleration during these first ten seconds.
From 10 to 16 seconds he maintained a constant velocity of
$8\,\text{m/sec}^{-1}$.
He then decelerates uniformly, coming to a stop after 30
seconds.

(b) Work out the total distance he travelled.

(c) Work out his deceleration between 16 and 30 seconds.

4 Jenny cycles at a constant acceleration of $1.2\,\text{m/sec}^{-2}$ for a
period of 20 seconds. She then travels for the next 40 seconds at
a constant velocity equal to the maximum speed she achieved
during the first 20 seconds.

(a) Draw an accurate velocity-time graph of her journey during
these 60 seconds.

(b) Work out the distances she travelled during these 60
seconds.

5 Work out the area bounded by the x-axis and the curve with
equation $x^2 + y^2 = 25$.
Give your answer correct to 1 decimal place.

6 Work out the area bounded by:

the positive x-axis,
the positive y-axis,
the curve with equation $x^2 + y^2 = 1$;
and the curve with equation $x^2 + y^2 = 9$.

Leave your answer in terms of π.

7 Solve the equations:

$$x + y = 2$$
$$x^2 + y^2 = 36$$

Leave your answer in surd form.

8 Solve the equations:

$$9x^2 - y^2 = 80$$
$$3x - y = 10$$

9 Solve the equations:

$$y - x = 1, \quad y = x^2 - 1$$

10 Prove that the equations:

$$y = ax - 3 \quad \text{and} \quad x^2 + y^2 = 25$$

must have two solutions in x and y for all values of a.

If your answer is incorrect, review in the Higher book:

1 The equation of a straight line, L, is
$$y = -\tfrac{1}{3}x + 5$$

(a) A line M is parallel to L and passes through the point $(0, -2)$.
Work out the equation of M.
(b) A line N is perpendicular to L and it passes through the point $(-1, 0)$.
Work out the equation of N.

Unit 7, Section 7.2
Unit 7, Section 7.2 and 7.3

2 Work out the area bounded by:
the positive x-axis,
the line $y = x$, and
the curve with equation $x^2 + y^2 = 100$
Leave your answer in terms of π.

Unit 19, Example 3
Unit 8, Example 5 and
Unit 19 Example 3

3 Solve the equation:
$$2x + y = 1$$
$$y = x^2 - 2$$

Unit 21, Example 16

4 The diagram represents a velocity-time graph for a moving object over a two-minute period.

Unit 27, Example 11
Unit 18, Section 18.7

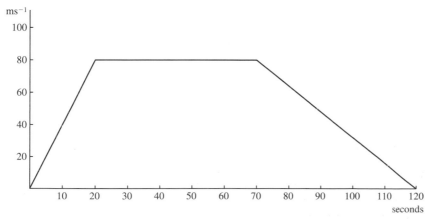

Calculate the distance travelled by this moving object during the two minutes.

Answers to Test yourself

1 **(a)** $y = -\tfrac{1}{3}x - 2$ **(b)** $y = 3x + 3$ **2** 25π sq. units **3** $x = -3, y = 7$ **4** $6800\,\text{m}$
$x = 1, y = -1$

11 Modelling

Solving real life problems mathematically and obtaining relationships between two sets of data is called mathematical modelling.

Key points to remember

1 The function $f(x) = a^x$, where a is a positive constant and x is a variable, is called an exponential function.

- If $a > 1$ then a^x is an example of exponential growth with a multiplier of a.
- If $0 < a < 1$ then a^x is an example of exponential decay with a multiplier of a.

2 A point lies on a curve if the coordinates of the point satisfy the equation of the curve.

3 To determine if the experimental results satisfy a given formula, reduce the formula to the form $Y = mX + c$. Plot Y against X and if the points lie approximately on a straight line the formula is confirmed.

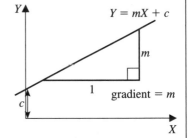

- To test $y = px + q$, plot y against x
- To test $y = px^2 + q$, plot y against x^2
- To test $y = px^2 + qx$, plot $\dfrac{y}{x}$ against x

Then if the points lie approximately on a straight line

- p is the gradient
- q is the intercept

Example 1
The table shows the value of a computer after each year

(y) Year	0	1	2	3	4	5	6
(v) Value	1500	1000	667	444	296	198	132

It is thought the relationship between y and v is of the form $v = pq^y$

(a) Draw a graph of y against v.
(b) Use your graph to find p and q and state the relationship between y and v.
(c) What type of relationship is shown?

Answer

(a)

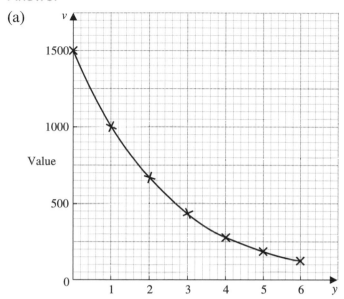

(b) Using **2**

Choose two points, say (0, 1500) and (1, 1000)

These must satisfy $\qquad v = pq^y$

Substitute (0, 1500) $\qquad 1500 = pq^0$

so $\qquad 1500 = p \times 1$

so $\qquad p = 1500$

Substitute (1, 1000) $\qquad 1000 = pq$

But $p = 1500$ so $\qquad 1000 = 1500\,q$

so $\qquad q = \frac{2}{3}$

so $\qquad v = 1500\,(\frac{2}{3})^y$

(c) Using **1** this type of relationship is exponential decay.

Worked examination question [E]

The table shows the distance, s metres, travelled by an object from the point P in t seconds.

t (seconds)	0.5	1.0	1.5	2.0	2.5
s (metres)	1.125	1.2	1.325	1.5	1.725

It is thought the relationship between s and t has the form $s = at^2 + b$, where a and b are constants.

(a) Confirm the relationship by plotting a suitable graph.

(b) Use the graph to estimate the values of a and b.

Answer

(a) Using **3**

Compare $\qquad s = at^2 + b$

with $\qquad Y = mX + c$

then $\qquad Y = s; X = t^2; m = a,$ and $c = b$

Plotting s on the vertical axis and t^2 on the horizontal axis should lead to a straight line to confirm the relationship.

Using the values of t in the given table to find t^2, form a table of values of t^2 against s.

t^2	0.25	1	2.25	4	6.25
s	1.125	1.2	1.325	1.5	1.725

Draw a graph using these values.

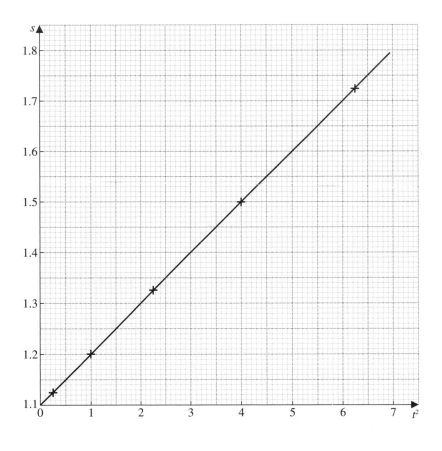

The points do not always lie exactly on a straight line. You may need to draw a line of best fit.

(b) Using **3**
     Taking two points on the line (1, 1.2) and (4, 1.5)

$$m = a = \text{gradient} = \frac{1.5 - 1.2}{4 - 1} = \frac{0.3}{3} = 0.1$$

and y intercept

$$c = b = 1.1$$

So $s = 0.1\,t^2 + 1.1$

Revision exercise 11

1 This sketch shows part of the graph $y = pq^x$.
Find p and q and state the formula.

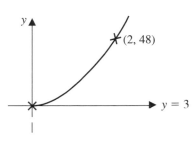

2 The sketch shows part of the graph $y = pq^x$.
Find p and q and state the formula.

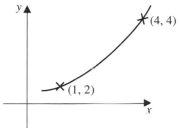

3 The value of a motorcycle decreases as shown in the table.

Years old (y)	0	1	2	3	4	5	6
Value (v)	5000	3000	1800	1080	648	389	233

(a) Draw a graph to confirm the relationship $v = pq^y$
(b) Use your graph to find p and q.

4

x	3	5	6	9	10
y	7	13	15	23	26

The table shows corresponding values of x and y.
The relationship between y and x is thought to be of the form
$y = ax + b$.
(a) Confirm the relationship by drawing a suitable graph.
(b) Use your graph to estimate the values of a and b.

5

x	1	2	3	4	5	6
y	40	65	100	145	200	265

The data is thought to be approximately equal to the
relationship $y = ax^2 + b$.
(a) Confirm the relationship by drawing a suitable graph.
(b) Use your graph to estimate the values of a and b.

6

x	1	2	3	4	5	6
y	3.7	12.4	26.1	44.8	68.5	97.2

The data is thought to be approximately equal to $y = ax^2 + bx$
(a) Draw a suitable graph to confirm the relationship.
(b) Use your graph to estimate the values of a and b.

7 A ball is dropped from a window. The time t seconds taken for the ball to fall a distance d feet is measured and recorded in the table below:

d	5	8	15	18	20	25
t	0.56	0.71	0.97	1.06	1.12	1.25
t^2						

(a) (i) Copy the table and complete the t^2 row.
  (ii) Draw the graph of d against t^2 for $0 \leqslant d \leqslant 30$ and $0 \leqslant t^2 \leqslant 1.6$.
  Explain how the graph indicates that $d = kt^2$ where k is a constant.

(b) Estimate the value of k to the nearest whole number.

[E, part]

Test yourself   What to review

1 The sketch shows part of the graph $y = pq^x$
  Find the values of p and q.

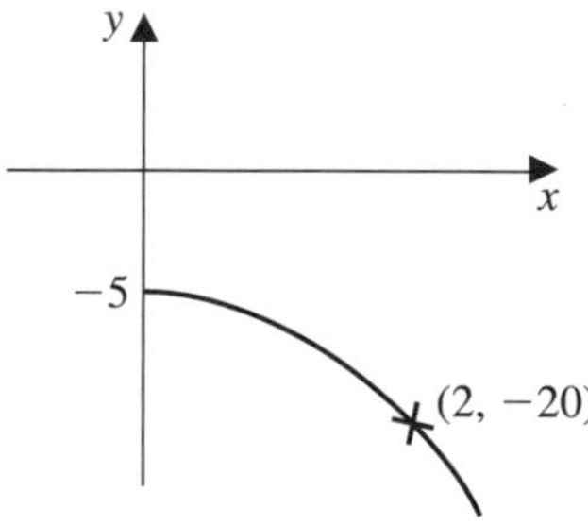

If your answer is incorrect, review in the Higher book:

Unit 30, Example 8
Unit 28, Example 8

2

x	1	2	3	4	5
y	−0.4	4.4	12.4	23.6	38

The relationship between x and y is $y = ax^2 + b$
Find a and b.

Unit 30, Example 6
Unit 28, Example 6

3

x	3	4	5	6	7
y	10.2	15.6	22	29.4	37.8

The relationship between x and y is $y = ax^2 + bx$
Find a and b.

Unit 30, Example 7
Unit 28, Example 7

Answers to Test yourself

1 $p = -5$, $q = 2$ 2 $a = 1.6$, $b = -2$ 3 $a = 0.5$, $b = 1.9$

12 Pythagoras and trigonometry

Pythagoras' theorem is used to find the third side of a right-angled triangle when the lengths of the other two sides are known. Trigonometry is used to find the length of a side or the size of an angle in a right-angled triangle.

Key points to remember

1 For any right-angled triangle, the formula for Pythagoras' theorem is
$$a^2 + b^2 = c^2$$
where c is the hypotenuse.

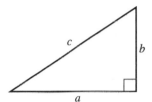

2 Pythagoras' theorem can be applied to problems set in three dimensions.
Always make a sketch of the triangle you need to use to answer the question.

3 The three trigonometric ratios are:

$$\sin \theta = \frac{\text{opp}}{\text{hyp}}$$

$$\cos \theta = \frac{\text{adj}}{\text{hyp}}$$

$$\tan \theta = \frac{\text{opp}}{\text{adj}}$$

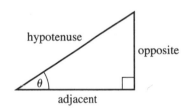

4 Trigonometry problems can be set in three dimensions.

5 Bearings are angles measured clockwise from North and expressed in three digits.

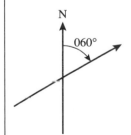
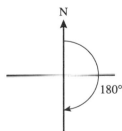
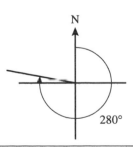

6 Angles of elevation and depression are measured from the horizontal.

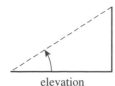

elevation

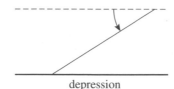

depression

Example 1

$VABC$ is a tetrahedron.
The base ABC is a triangle.
The angle $ABC = 90°$
The vertex V is vertically above B

$$AB = 7\,\text{cm} \qquad BC = 24\,\text{cm} \qquad VA = 18\,\text{cm}$$

(a)   Calculate the lengths of
     (i) AC (ii) VB
(b)   Calculate the angles
     (i) ACB (ii) BAV

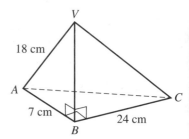

Answer

(a)   (i)   Using **1** and **2**
           look at the base ABC.
$$AC^2 = AB^2 + BC^2$$
$$= 7^2 + 24^2$$
$$= 49 + 576$$
$$= 625$$
So $AC = \sqrt{625}$
$$= 25\,\text{cm}$$

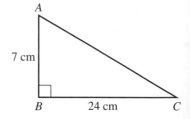

(ii)   Using **1** and **2**
       look at the plane face VBA.
$$VA^2 = AB^2 + VB^2$$
$$18^2 = 7^2 + VB^2$$
$$324 = 49 + VB^2$$
$$324 - 49 = VB^2$$
So $VB^2 = 275$
$$VB = \sqrt{275}$$
$$= 16.58\,\text{cm}\ (2\,\text{d.p.})$$

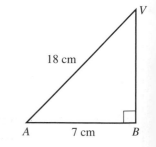

(b)   (i)   Using **4**
           look again at the base ABC.
           Using **3**

$$\tan ACB = \frac{7}{24}$$
$$\tan ACB = 0.291\,66$$
$$ACB = 16.26°$$

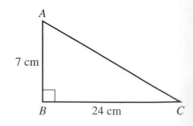

(b) (ii) Using ▨**4**
look again at the face VBA
Using ▨**3**

$$\cos BAV = \frac{7}{18}$$
$$= 0.3888\ldots$$
$$\text{angle } BAV = 67.11°$$

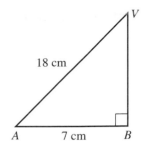

Worked examination question [E]

The diagram shows the path taken by a yacht.
The yacht leaves a harbour H.
It travels 45 km due North to a marker buoy B.
At B the yacht turns and travels a further 32 km due East to a
lighthouse L.
At L the yacht turns again and travels in a straight line back to the
harbour H.
(a) Calculate the total distance travelled by the yacht.
(b) Calculate the bearing of L from H.

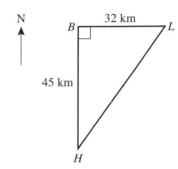

On its return journey from L to H the yacht passes through a point
P.
This point P is the point on the line LH such that the yacht is at its
closest point, on the return journey, to the marker buoy B.
(c) Calculate the distance from P to B.
(d) Calculate the bearing of P from B.

Answer
(a) Using ▨**1** calculate LH
$$LH^2 = HB^2 + BL^2$$
$$= 45^2 + 32^2$$
$$= 2025 + 1024$$
$$= 3049$$
$$LH = 55.22 \text{ km}$$
So the total distance travelled by the yacht is
$$45 + 32 + 55.22 = 132.22 \text{ km}$$

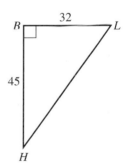

(b) Using ▨**3** and ▨**5**
find the angle x

$$\tan x = \frac{32}{45} = 0.471\,11\ldots$$
$$x = 35.4°$$
So the bearing of L from H is 035° to the nearest degree.

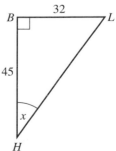

(c) *P* must be on *LH*. For *PB* to be the minimum distance, *BP* must be perpendicular to *LH*.

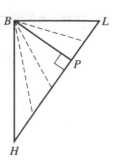

Using **3**

$$\sin x = \frac{BP}{BH}$$

$$\sin 35.4 = \frac{BP}{45}$$

So $BP = 45 \times \sin 35.4$
$$= 45 \times 0.57928$$
$$= 26.07 \, \text{km}$$

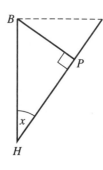

(d) Find the angle *NBP*.
$$\text{Angle } NBP = x + 90°$$
$$= 35.4° + 90°$$
$$= 125.4°$$
The bearing of *P* from *B* is 125° to the nearest degree.

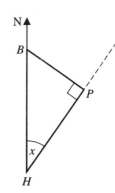

Example 2

In the triangle *ABC*, $AC = 15$ cm, angle $ABC = 62°$ and angle $BAC = 90°$
Calculate the length of *BC*.

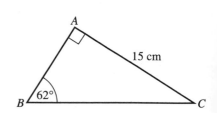

Answer
Using **3**

$$\frac{15}{BC} = \sin 62°$$

So $\dfrac{15}{\sin 62°} = BC$

So $BC = 16.99$ cm.

Revision exercise 12

1 The diagram shows a triangle PQR
$$PQ = 6\,\text{cm} \qquad RQ = 18\,\text{cm}$$
Calculate
(a) the perimeter of the triangle PQR
(b) the area of the triangle PQR
(c) the angle marked.   [E]

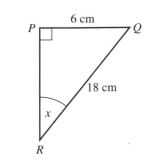
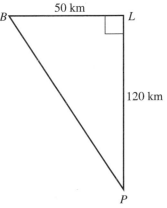

2 The diagram shows the path taken by a ship.
The ship leaves a port P.
It sails 120 km due North to a lighthouse L.
At L the ship turns due West and travels a further 50 km due West to a marker buoy B.

At B the ship turns again and travels back to P in a straight line.

Calculate
(a) the total distance travelled by the ship.
(b) the bearing of B from P.
(c) the shortest distance between the ship and L on the ship's return journey from B to P.

Diagram not accurately drawn

3 The diagram represents a cuboid $ABCDEFGH$.
$$AB = 6\,\text{cm} \qquad BC = 15\,\text{cm} \qquad CD = 5\,\text{cm}$$
Calculate
(a) the length of BG.
(b) the length of BE.
(c) the angle between BE and BG.

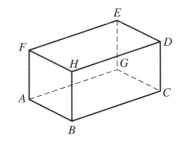

4

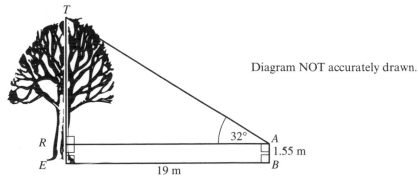

Diagram NOT accurately drawn.

Abbi is standing on level ground, at B, a distance of 19 metres away from the foot E of a tree TE.

She measures the angle of elevation of the top of the tree at a height of 1.55 metres above the ground as $32°$.
Calculate the height TE of the tree. Give your answer correct to 3 significant figures.   [E]

5 The diagram shows a wedge *ABCDEF*.
The horizontal base *BCDE* is a rectangle
$$BC = 15\,\text{cm} \qquad CD = 24\,\text{cm}$$
The face *ABEF* is in the vertical plane.
Angle *ABC* = Angle *FED* = 90°
$$AC = FD = 17\,\text{cm}$$
Calculate

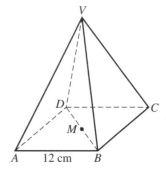

(a) the length of *AB*   (b) the length of *CE*
(c) the angle *ACB*   (d) the angle *FCE*

6 *VABCD* is a pyramid.
The base *ABCD* is a square.
The vertex *V* is vertically above point *M*, the centre of the base.
$$VB = 25\,\text{cm} \qquad AB = 12\,\text{cm}$$
Calculate
(a) the length of *AC*
(b) the length of *BM*
(c) the angle *VBM*.

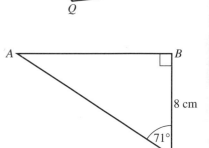

7 *SPQR* is a tetrahedron.
The base *PQR* is a triangle, with angle *PQR* = 90°
The vertex *S* is vertically above *Q*.
$$SR = 41\,\text{cm} \qquad SQ = 40\,\text{cm} \qquad PQ = 12\,\text{cm}$$

Calculate
(a) the angle *QRS*   (b) the length of *QR*
(c) the length of *PR*   (d) the angle *SPQ*.

8 *ABC* is a triangle with angle *ABC* = 90°, angle *BCA* = 71°
and the length of *BC* is 8 cm.

Work out the length of *AC*.

9 Right angled triangles can have sides with lengths which are a
rational or irrational number of units.
Give an example of a right angled triangle to fit each description
below.
  (i) All sides are rational
 (ii) The hypotenuse is rational and the other two sides are
     irrational.
(iii) The hypotenuse is irrational and the other two sides are
     rational.
(iv) The hypotenuse and one of the other two sides are rational
     and the remaining side is irrational.   [E]

Test yourself	**What to review**

1 The diagram shows the path taken by a man on a walk.
The man leaves his home *H* and walks 4.3 km due North to a
stile *S*.
At *S* he turns due West and walks a further 2.2 km to a
crossroads *C*.
At *C* he turns again and walks back to his home in a straight
line.

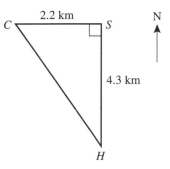

*If your answer is incorrect,
review in the Higher book:*

(a) Calculate the total distance walked by the man.
Give your answer in kilometres, correct to 2 d.p.

Unit 8, Example 2
Unit 8, Example 2

(b) Calculate the bearing of *C* from *H*.
Give your answer correct to the nearest degree.

Unit 13, Example 4
Unit 13, Example 4

---

2 *ABCDEFGH* is a cuboid.
 AB = 5 cm   *BC* = 12 cm   *AF* = 8 cm

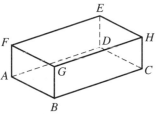

(a) Calculate the length of *FB*.
Give your answer in cm correct to 2 d.p.

Unit 8, Example 8
Unit 8, Example 8

(b) Calculate the length of the diagonal *BE*.
Give your answer in cm correct to 2 d.p.

Unit 8, Example 8
Unit 8, Example 8

(c) Calculate the value of the angle *FBA*.
Give your answer correct to the nearest degree.

Unit 22, Example 9
Unit 22, Example 9

(d) Calculate the value of the angle *EBF*.
Give your answer correct to the nearest degree.

Unit 22, Example 9
Unit 22, Example 9

Answers to Test yourself

1 **(a)** 11.33 km **(b)** 333°   **2** **(a)** 9.43 cm **(b)** 15.26 cm **(c)** 58° **(d)** 52°

13 Similarity and enlargement

Two shapes are similar when they look the same but one is bigger than the other.

Key points to remember

1 Shapes are similar if one shape is an enlargement of the other.

2 When two shapes are similar the corresponding sides are in proportion and corresponding angles are equal.

3 The scale factor of enlargement is the ratio:

$$\frac{\text{length of a side on one shape}}{\text{length of corresponding side on the other shape}}$$

4 An enlargement can have a positive, negative or fractional scale factor.
The image will be reduced if the scale factor is smaller than 1.
A negative scale factor indicates that the measuring from the centre of enlargement must be in the opposite direction.
To describe an enlargement, state the centre and the scale factor.

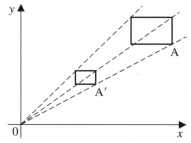

A' is an enlargement of A, scale factor $\frac{1}{2}$, centre the origin.

5 If the scale factor is ± 1, the two shapes are identical and are said to be congruent.

6 When the scale factor of the length of two similar shapes is k, then the scale factor of the areas of the two shapes is k^2 (and the scale factor of volumes is k^3).

Example 1

The vertices of triangle ABC are at the points
$$A\,(2,2) \qquad B\,(4,2) \qquad C\,(2,6)$$

The image of ABC after an enlargement scale factor $-1\frac{1}{2}$ centre $(0,0)$ is $A'B'C'$.

Work out the coordinates of $A'B'C'$.

Answer

Image after an enlargement centre $(0,0)$ scale factor $-1\frac{1}{2}$.

Using **4** the 'negative' enlargement goes in the 'opposite' direction.

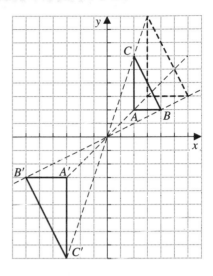

To find the coordinates of the image when the centre is the origin, multiply the coordinates by the scale factor, so

$A = (2,2)$ becomes $A' = (2 \times -1\frac{1}{2}, 2 \times -1\frac{1}{2}) = (-3,-3)$.

$B = (4,2)$ becomes $B' = (4 \times -1\frac{1}{2}, 2 \times -1\frac{1}{2}) = (-6,-3)$.

$C = (2,6)$ becomes $C' = (2 \times -1\frac{1}{2}, 6 \times -1\frac{1}{2}) = (-3,-9)$.

So A' is $(-3,-3)$, B' is $(-6,-3)$, C' is $(-3,-9)$

Worked examination question [E]

In the diagram $FG = 5.6$ metres, $EH = 3.5$ metres and $DH = 15$ metres. EH is parallel to FG.
FED and DHG are straight lines.

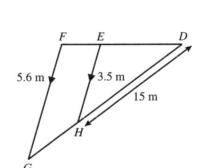

Calculate
(a) the length of DG.
(b) the ratio of the areas of triangles DEH and DFG.

Answer

(a) For triangles DEH and DFG
   $\hat{D}$ is common to both.
   $\hat{E} = \hat{F}$; $\hat{H} = \hat{G}$ (parallel lines)
   So using **2** these two triangles are similar.
   Using **3** the scale factor of the enlargement is

$$\frac{FG}{EH} = \frac{5.6}{3.5} = 1.6$$

So, using **3** again

$$\frac{DG}{DH} = \text{scale factor} = 1.6$$

$$\frac{DG}{15} = 1.6$$

$$DG = 15 \times 1.6 = 24\,\text{cm}$$

(b) Using **6** ratio of lengths $= 1:1.6$
   so ratio of areas $\qquad = 1:1.6^2$
   $\qquad\qquad\qquad\quad\; = 1:2.56$
   $\qquad\qquad\qquad\quad\; = 25:64$

Revision exercise 13

1 Zoe wanted to find the height of a tower in the park.
She placed a 1.6 m pole upright in the shadow of the tower. The
end of the shadow of the pole was in the same place as the end
of the shadow of the tower.
Her brother Andrew then took measurements. The
measurements are shown in the diagram.

Use the measurements to calculate the height, h metres, of the
tower.   **[E]**

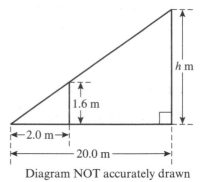

Diagram NOT accurately drawn

2 In the diagram angle ABC = angle CDE = angle CEF = 65°
and   length $AB = 3$ cm
          length $AC = 4$ cm
          length $CE = 7$ cm
(a) Calculate the length DE.
(b) Write down two triangles which are similar to triangle
    ABC.   **[E]**

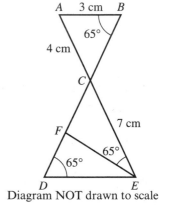

Diagram NOT drawn to scale

3 Triangle PQR has its vertices at
        $P(4, 7)$ $Q(7, 7)$ $R(7, 13)$
PQR is enlarged by a scale factor of $-\frac{1}{3}$ centre $(1, 1)$ to form
$P'Q'R'$.

Find the coordinates of P', Q' and R'.

4 AC is parallel to XY.
        $AC = 7$ cm, $XY = 4$ cm, $AB = 12$ cm
(a) Explain why the triangles ABC and XBY are similar.
(b) Calculate the length of XB.
(c) Calculate the ratio:

        $$\frac{\text{area } ABC}{\text{area } XBY}$$ **[E]**

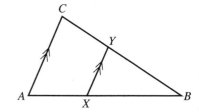

5 A shape S is transformed by an enlargement scale factor $-k$,
centre P to form an image S'.

S' is then transformed by a scale factor $\frac{1}{k}$, centre Q to form a
second image S''.

Explain whether or not S and S'' are congruent.

6 *ABC* is a triangle with *CAB* = 90°.
AP is perpendicular to *BC*.
P lies on *BC*.

$$AB = 12\,\text{cm}, \qquad AC = 5\,\text{cm}$$

Calculate the length of *AP*, giving your reasons.

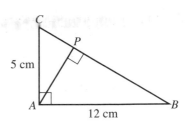

Test yourself	**What to review**

1 *PQ* is parallel to *ST*.
PQ = 3 cm,
TS = 8 cm,
RT = 12 cm

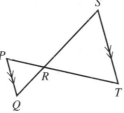

*If your answer is incorrect,
review in the Higher book:*

(a) Explain why triangles *PQR* and *TSR* are similar.

Unit 3, Section 3.9
Unit 3, Section 3.9

(b) Calculate the length of *PR*.

Unit 3, Example 7
Unit 3, Example 7

(c) Calculate the ratio

$$\frac{\text{area } PQR}{\text{area } TSR}$$

Unit 19, Section 19.3
Unit 19, Section 19.3

2 Triangle *OA′B′* is formed by enlarging triangle *OAB*, centre *O*.

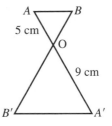

(a) Comment on the correctness of the statement
    'The scale factor of the enlargement is 1.8'

Unit 6

(b) Copy the diagram and show clearly where a line segment *XY*
    should be drawn so that triangle *OAB* and *OXY* are congruent.

Unit 3, Section 3.8

Answers to Test yourself

1 **(a)** $\hat{R}$ is common, $\hat{Q} = \hat{S}$ $\hat{P} = \hat{T}$ **(b)** $4\frac{1}{2}$ cm **(c)** $\frac{9}{64}$ **2** **(a)** The scale factor should be −1.8.   **(b)**

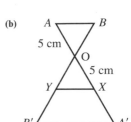

14 Loci, constructions and congruency

Geometrical shapes can be constructed on the paths taken by moving points.

Key points to remember

1 The path taken by a point which moves is called the locus of the point.

2 Some geometrical shapes and/or loci can be formally constructed using a pencil, compass and a straight edge.

3 Two shapes which are identical in every respect are said to be congruent.

4 The conditions under which two triangles are congruent are:

SSS   All three sides equal in length
SAS   Two sides and their included angles equal
SAA   One side equal and two angles equal.

Worked examination question 1 [E]

A point P moves on the outside of the rectangle $ABCD$ such that the shortest distance from P to $ABCD$ is always 2 cm.
Draw the locus of P.

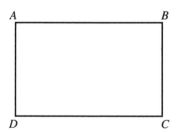

Answer

Start at A.

P moves parallel to AB at a distance of 2 cm.

On reaching B, the point P will move in a quarter circle, centre B, of radius 2 cm, i.e.:

It creates the above process to give a final locus, i.e.:

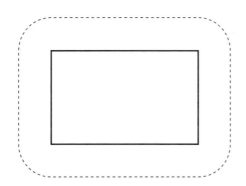

Example 1

(a) Using pencil, compass and a straight edge, construct the perpendicular bisector of AB.

The midpoint of AB is M.

(b) Construct the angle AMP where

$< AMP = 135°$.

Answer

It is important to show all construction work.

(a)

gives perpendicular bisector

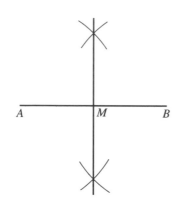

(b)

Bisect the right angle at M.

i.e.

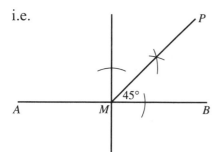

to create $< PMB = 45°$

So

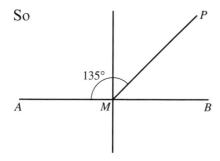

angle $AMP = 135°$

Worked examination question 2

$ABCD$ is a parallelogram with diagonal AC.
Prove that the triangles ABC and CDA
   are congruent.

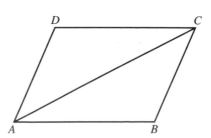

Answer

$A\widehat{C}B = D\widehat{A}C$ (‖ lines, alternate)
$B\widehat{A}C = D\widehat{C}A$ (‖ lines, alternate)

AC is common to both triangles.

Hence

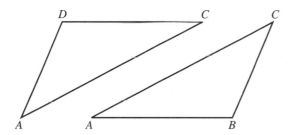

ABC and CDA congruent SAA.

Revision exercise 14

1   A———————————B

A point P moves so that the shortest distance from P to the line
segment AB is 3 cm.
Draw the locus of P.

2 A and B are two points 6 cm apart.

A point, P, lies in the plane and is such that

$PA \leqslant 4$ cm
$PA \geqslant PB$ cm

Construct accurately the region in which P can lie.

3 AB is a line segment.
P is a point not on AB.
$PA > PB$.

•P

The bisector of the angle PAB meets the
perpendicular from P to AB at the point M.

Showing all your construction work, find the accurate position
of M.

4

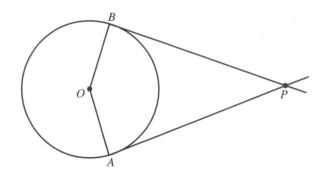

PA and PB are tangents from a point P to a circle centre O.

Prove that the triangles POA and POB are congruent.

5

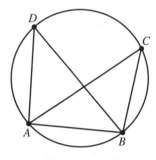

Points ABCD lie on a circle.

angle $B\widehat{A}C$ = angle $A\widehat{B}D$

Prove that the triangles ABC and BAD are congruent.

Test yourself   **What to review**

If your answer is incorrect, review in the Higher book:

1 ABC is an equilateral triangle with sides of length 5 cm.

A point P lies outside ABC. P moves so that the shortest distance from P to the triangle is always 2 cm.

Draw the locus of P.

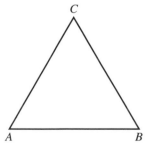

Unit 6, Example 11
Unit 6, Example 11

---

2 Using a pencil, straight edge and compass, construct an angle of 30°.

Unit 6, Example 15

3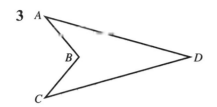

ABCD is an
arrowhead (delta).

Unit 3, Section 3.8
Unit 3, Example 6

Prove that the triangles *ABD* and *CBD* are congruent.

Answers to Test yourself

1

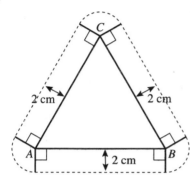

2

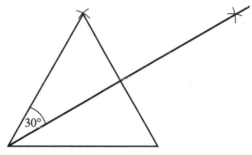

First draw a straight line.
Use a compass to construct an equilateral triangle (each angle is 60°).
Use a compass to find the midpoint of one of the edges.
Draw a straight line from the midpoint to the opposite angle,
i.e. cutting the 60° angle in half to make a 30° angle.

3 Side *BD* is common to both triangles; angle $C\hat{D}B$ = angle $A\hat{D}B$; angle $A\hat{B}D$ = angle $C\hat{B}D$ ⇒ DAA.

15 Advanced trigonometry

Key points to remember

1 Area of triangle $= \frac{1}{2}ab\sin C$

2 The Sine Rule

$$\frac{a}{\sin A} = \frac{b}{\sin B} = \frac{c}{\sin C}$$

and

$$\frac{\sin A}{a} = \frac{\sin B}{b} = \frac{\sin C}{c}$$

3 The Cosine Rule

$$c^2 = a^2 + b^2 - 2ab\cos C$$

and

$$\cos C = \frac{a^2 + b^2 - c^2}{2ab}$$

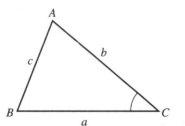

Worked examination question [E]

A farmer fences off a triangular field PQR.

$$PQ = 64\,\text{m} \qquad PR = 43\,\text{m}$$
Angle $QPR = 72°$

Calculate
(a) the area of the field
(b) the perimeter of the field
(c) the angle PQR.

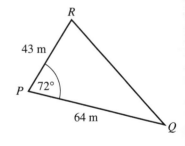

Answer

(a) Using **1**
Area $= \frac{1}{2} \times 64 \times 43 \times \sin 72°$
$= 1308.65\,\text{m}^2$

(b) Perimeter $= 64\,\text{m} + 43\,\text{m} + RQ$
Using **3**
$$RQ^2 = 64^2 + 43^2 - 2 \times 64 \times 43 \times \cos 72°$$
$$= 4096 + 1849 - 1700.83$$
$$= 5945 - 1700.83 = 4244.17$$
$$RQ = \sqrt{4244.17} = 65.15\,\text{m}$$

So perimeter $= 64 + 43 + 65.15 = 172.15\,\text{m}$

(c) Using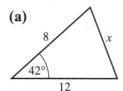

$$\frac{\sin PQR}{43} = \frac{\sin 72°}{65.15}$$

$$\sin PQR = \frac{43 \times \sin 72°}{65.15}$$

$$= 0.6277$$

$$\text{Angle } PQR = 38.88°$$

Example 1

In the triangle ABC opposite, work out the size of the angle marked θ.

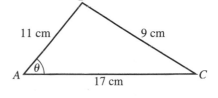

Answer

Using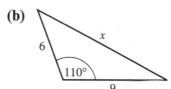

$$\cos \theta = \frac{17^2 + 11^2 - 9^2}{2 \times 17 \times 11}$$

$$\cos \theta = \frac{329}{374}$$

so $\qquad \theta = 28.4°$ (1 d.p.)

Revision exercise 15

1 In each of these triangles the lengths are in centimetres. For each triangle, calculate the area and the length of the side marked x.

(a)

8
x
42°
12

(b)

6
x
110°
9

2 Two ships leave port C.

Ship P travels on a bearing of $060°$ for $13\,\text{km}$ to A.
Ship Q travels on a bearing of $315°$ for $17\,\text{km}$ to B.
Calculate the bearing of B from A.

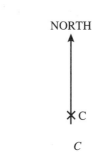

3 Speedboats race around the triangular circuit A to B to C to A as shown in the diagram.
$$AB = 5.0\,\text{km}, BC = 7.0\,\text{km and angle } BAC = 60°$$
$$AC = x\,\text{km}$$

(a) Using the Cosine Rule, show that
$$x^2 - 5x - 24 = 0$$

The speedboats are taking part in a $100\,\text{km}$ race.

(b) By calculating the value of x, work out how many times around the circuit, ABC, the speedboats should travel. **[E]**

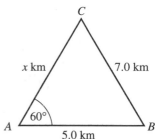

4

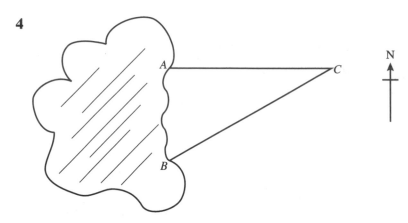

On this island, Port *A* is due North of Port *B*.
A ship leaves Port *B* and travels on a bearing of 060° for 50 km.
The ship is now due East of *A* at point *C*.
(a) Calculate the distance from Port *A* to point *C*.

At the same time as the first ship leaves Port *B*, another ship
leaves port *A* on a bearing of 145°. Both ships travel at constant
speeds and meet after 2 hours.
(b) Calculate the speed of each ship.   [E]

5 In the diagram, *XY* represents a vertical tower on level ground.
A and *B* are points due West of *Y*.
The distance *AB* is 30 metres.

The angle of elevation of *X* from *A* is 30°.
The angle of elevation of *X* from *B* is 50°.

Calculate the height, in metres, of the tower *XY*.
Give your answer correct to 1 decimal place.   [E]

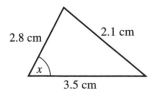

Diagram NOT accurately drawn

6 Calculate the angle marked *x*.

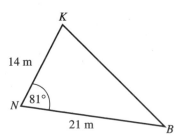

2.8 cm   2.1 cm

x

3.5 cm

7

K

14 m

N   81°

21 m   B

(a) Calculate the length *KB*.
(b) Calculate the size of the angle *NKB*   [E]

8 In a triangle PQR

$PQ = 12\,\text{cm}$, $PR = 8\,\text{cm}$ and the area of $PQR = 38\,\text{cm}^2$.

(a) Calculate the two possible values for the angle QPR.

(b) In both cases calculate the length of QR.

9 A ship, S, leaves a harbour, H.
The ship travels 42 km due North until it reaches a marker buoy B.
At B the ship turns on a bearing of $073°$ and travels for a further 70 km until it reaches a lighthouse L.
At L the ship turns again and travels back to H in a straight line.
Calculate

(a) the total distance travelled by the ship.

(b) the bearing of L from H.

(c) the shortest distance between S and B on the ship's return journey from L to H.

10

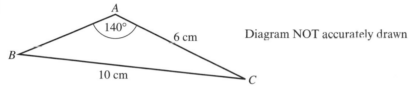

$AC = 6\,\text{cm}$, $BC = 10\,\text{cm}$, Angle $\widehat{BAC} = 140°$.
Calculate angle ACB. Give your answer to the nearest tenth of a degreee.　　　　　　　　　　　　　　　[E]

Test yourself　　　　　　　　　　　　　　**What to review**

1 The town of Lucea is 18 km due North of the town of Preble. The town of Manwell is 24 km from Preble on a bearing of $340°$ from Preble.
The towns are joined by three straight roads.

(a) Calculate the distance from Lucea to Manwell.

(b) Calculate the area enclosed by the three roads.

(c) Calculate the bearing of Lucea from Manwell.

If your answer is incorrect, review in the Higher book:

Unit 22, Example 7
Unit 22, Example 7
Unit 22, Examples 1 and 2
Unit 22, Examples 1 and 2
Unit 22, Example 5
Unit 6, Example 2

Answers to Test yourself

1 **(a)** 9.39 km　　　**(b)** 73.88 km^2　　　**(c)** 119°

16 Trigonometry: angles greater than 90°

Trigonometry can be extended to angles of all sizes.

Key points to remember

1 The graph of sin x *is*

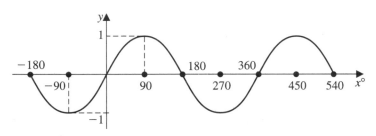

2 The graph of cos x *is*

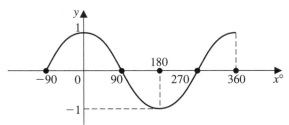

3 The graph of tan x *is*

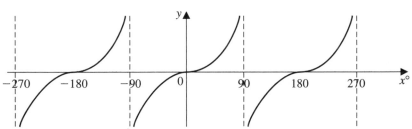

4 You need to be able to solve equations such as
$$\tan x = 2$$
for $0° \leqslant x \leqslant 360°$

Example 1
Find all solutions of the equation
$$3 \sin x° = 2$$
in the range $0° \leqslant x \leqslant 360°$

Answer

$$3 \sin x = 2$$
is the same as
$$\sin x = \tfrac{2}{3}$$

So, from the calculator, one solution is
$$x = 41.8° \text{ (to 1 d.p.)}$$

Using ■ the graph of sin x is

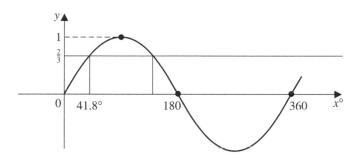

So in the range $0° \leqslant x \leqslant 360°$, the second solution to $\sin x = \frac{2}{3}$ is

$$x = 180 - 41.8 = 138.2°$$

The two solutions are

$$x = 41.8° \text{ and } x = 138.2°$$

(both correct to 1 d.p.)

Worked examination question [E]

Draw the graph of

$$y = 4 \cos x°$$

By drawing an appropriate straight line, find solutions of the equation

$$4 \cos x° = \frac{x°}{36} \text{ in the range } -180 \leqslant x \leqslant 180$$

Answer

Taking some values of x:

$x°$	$\cos x°$	$y = 4 \cos x°$
-180	-1	-4
-135	-0.707	-2.83
-90	0	0
-45	0.707	2.83
0	1	4
45	0.707	2.83
90	0	0
135	-0.707	-2.83
180	-1	-4

Using **2** the graph of $y = 4 \cos x°$ is

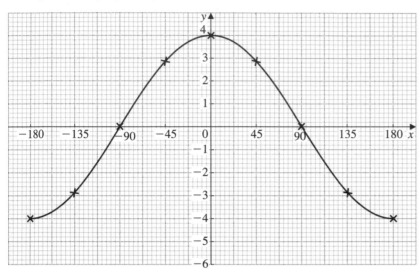

The solutions of

$$4 \cos x° = \frac{x°}{36}$$

occur at the points of intersection of

$$y = 4 \cos x° \text{ and } y = \frac{x°}{36}$$

On the graph draw

$$y = \frac{x°}{36}$$

which is a straight line passing through the points

$$x = 0, \quad y = 0,$$
$$x = 180°, \quad y = 5.$$

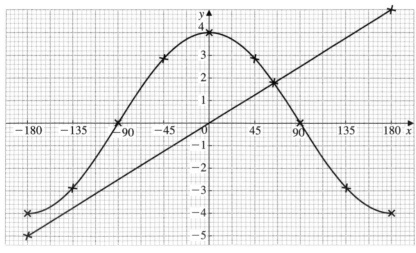

From the graph, the only solution is $x = 63.7°$.

Example 2

For all values of $x°$ in the range $0 \leqslant x < 360$, find the solutions of
$$\sin 3x° = \sin 60°$$

Answer

One solution is when
$$3x = 60° \text{ i.e. } x = 20°$$

Also $\sin 60° = 0.866$
So the solutions are when
$$\sin 3x = 0.866$$
Using ▮ the graph of $\sin 3x$ *is*

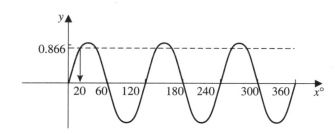

From the graph, the other solutions are
$$x = 20°, 40°, 140°, 160°, 260°, 280°.$$

> There is more information on sketching graphs in Unit 9.

Revision exercise 16

1 Find two different values of x *between 0 and 180 for which*
$$\sin (2x)° = \sin 30°$$ *[E]*

2 Draw the graph of
$$y = \cos 2x°$$
for $0 \leqslant x \leqslant 180$.

3 Work out all the solutions of
$$\tan x° = 3$$
in the range $0 \leqslant x \leqslant 180$.

4 Work out all the solutions of
$$2 \cos x° = 1$$
in the range $-360° \leqslant x \leqslant 360$.

5 Find the solutions of
$$\cos (2x)° = \cos 60°$$
in the range $-180 \leqslant x \leqslant 180$.

6 Sketch the graph of
$$y = \tan 2x°$$
for $0 \leqslant x \leqslant 180$.

7 Given that
$$y = 5 \sin x°$$
for $0 \leqslant x \leqslant 360$, find
(a) the maximum value of *y and the value of x for which y is a maximum.*
(b) the minimum value of *y and the value of x for which y is a minimum.*

8 Solve the equation
$$5 \cos x° = 3$$
in the range $-180° \leqslant x \leqslant 180°$.

Test yourself	What to review
	If your answer is incorrect, review in the Higher book:
1 Find two different values of *x between 0° and 360°* for which $3\cos x = 1$	*Unit 13, Example 11* Unit 13, Example 11
2 Draw the graph of $y = \sin 2x°$ for $0 \leqslant x \leqslant 180°$.	*Unit 13, page 248, Worked examination question* Unit 13, page 286, Worked examination question
3 Find the maximum value of $5 \sin 2x°$.	*Unit 13, page 248, Worked examination question* Unit 13, page 286, Worked examination question

Answers to Test yourself

1 $x = 70.5°, 289.5°$ **2**   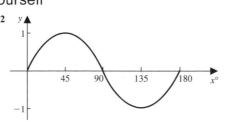   **3**   5

17 Combined transformations

It is possible to combine two (or more) transformations – such as reflections, rotations, enlargements – to create an equivalent single transformation.

Key points to remember

1 An object can be transformed by:

- a translation
- a reflection
- a rotation
- an enlargement

2 Two transformations can be combined to form a single equivalent transformation.

3 A reflection followed by a reflection can be replaced by the single transformation of:

- a rotation if the reflection lines are *not* parallel.
- a translation if the reflection lines are parallel.

Example 1

Triangle *A* is rotated through 90° in the anticlockwise direction about (1, 0) to give the image *B*.

B is then rotated through 90° in the anticlockwise direction about the origin to form the second image *C*.

Work out the single transformation which transforms *A* to *C*.

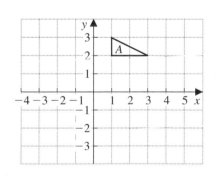

Answer

Rotating *A* about (1, 0) through 90° anticlockwise gives *B* as in the diagram.

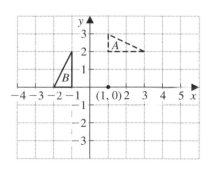

Then rotating B about $(0, 0)$ in the anticlockwise direction gives C.

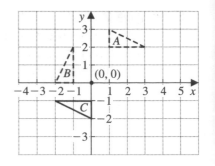

Using **2** the single transformation which transforms A to C is a rotation through $180°$.

The centre of the rotation is found at the intersection of the construction lines.

So the single transformation that transforms A to C is a rotation through $180°$ about $(\frac{1}{2}, \frac{1}{2})$.

Note: the single transformation could also be described as an enlargement, scale factor -1, centre $(\frac{1}{2}, \frac{1}{2})$.

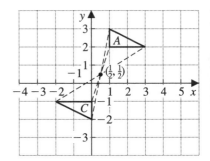

Worked examination question [E]

The triangle T is reflected in the y-axis to form the image S.

S is then reflected in the line $y = -x$ to form the second image U.

Find the single transformation which maps T to U.

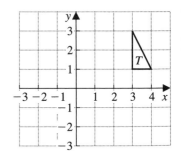

Answer

Reflecting T in the y-axis gives S, and then reflecting S in the line $y = -x$ gives U.

Using **3** the single transformation which maps T to U is a rotation about the origin through $90°$ in the anticlockwise direction.

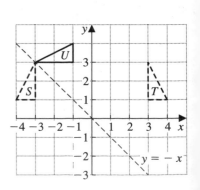

Example 2

The triangle A is reflected in the line L to form an image A'.
A' is then reflected in the line M to form a second image A''.
Work out the single transformation which maps A to A''.

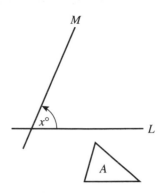

Answer

Reflecting A in L gives A'.

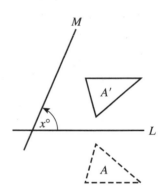

Reflecting A' in M gives A''.

The single transformation which maps A to A'' is a rotation about
the point of intersection of L and M, through $2x°$ in the
anticlockwise direction.

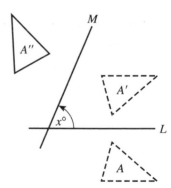

Revision exercise 17

1 Triangle T is reflected in the line $x = 3$ to produce the image S.

   S is then reflected in the line $x = 6$ to produce a second
   image U.

   Find the single transformation which maps
   (a) T to U
   (b) U to T.

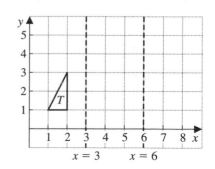

2 **(a)** Draw diagrams to show how the outcome of two successive reflections can be
either
   (i) a translation   or   **(ii)** a rotation.
(b) In case **(ii)** above, describe completely the rotation.

3 The triangle A is rotated about $(-1, 0)$ through $90°$ in the clockwise direction to produce the image A'.

A' is then rotated about $(0, 0)$ through $90°$ in the clockwise direction to produce the second image A''.

Find the single transformation which transforms
   (i) A to A''
  (ii) A'' to A.

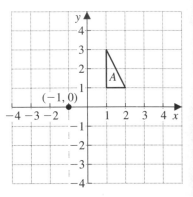

4 A shape S is reflected in the x-axis to produce an image S'.
S' is then reflected in the line $y = x$ to produce a second image S''.

Describe fully the single transformation which maps S to S''.

5 A triangle ABC has co-ordinates

$$A(1, 1)\quad B(2, 1)\quad C(1, 3).$$

ABC is enlarged by scale factor 2, centre $(0, 0)$ to produce an image $A'B'C'$.
$A'B'C'$ is then enlarged by scale factor 3, centre $(0, 0)$ to produce $A''B''C''$.

(a) Find the coordinates of the vertices of $A''B''C''$.
(b) Find the single transformation which maps ABC to $A''B''C''$.

6 A shape S is enlarged by a scale factor k, centre point X, to produce an image S'.
S' is then enlarged by a scale factor k, centre point X, to produce a second image S''.

Find the single transformation which maps
(a) S to S''
(b) S'' to S.

1 The diagram shows two lines L and M and a shape S.
The two lines L and M intersect at the point P.
The acute angle between L and M is $72°$.

S is reflected in L to produce an image S'.
S' is then reflected in M to produce a second image S''.

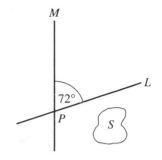

*If your answer is incorrect,
review in the Higher book:*

Describe fully the single transformation which maps S to S''.

Unit 6, Section 6.4
Unit 6, Section 6.4

---

2 Triangle T is rotated about $(0,0)$, through $90°$ in the clockwise
direction to produce an image T'.
T' is then rotated about $(0,0)$, through $45°$ in the clockwise
direction to produce a second
image T''.

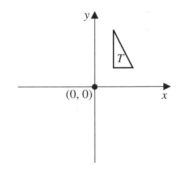

Describe fully the single transformation which maps T'' to T.

*Unit 6, Example 5 and Section
6.4*
Unit 6, Example 5 and
Section 6.4

Answers to Test yourself

1 Anticlockwise rotation about P through $144°$.
2 Rotation about $(0,0)$, through $135°$ in the anticlockwise direction.

18 Advanced mensuration

Key points to remember

1 The formulae for parts of a circle are:

- arc length $= \dfrac{\pi r \theta}{180}$

- area of sector $= \dfrac{\pi r^2 \theta}{360}$

- area of segment $= \dfrac{\pi r^2 \theta}{360} - \dfrac{1}{2} r^2 \sin \theta$

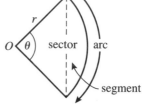

2 The formulae for a cylinder are:

- surface area $= 2\pi r h + 2\pi r^2$
- volume $= \pi r^2 h$

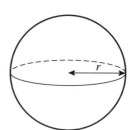

3 The volume of a pyramid or cone
$$= \frac{1}{3} \times \text{area of base} \times \text{vertical height}$$

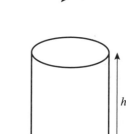

4 The formulae for a sphere are:

- volume $= \dfrac{4\pi r^3}{3}$

- surface area $= 4\pi r^2$

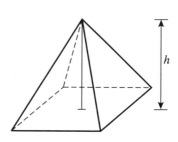

5 When a shape is enlarged by a scale factor k to produce a similar shape:

- area of enlarged shape $= k^2 \times$ area of original shape
- volume of enlarged shape
$$= k^3 \times \text{volume of original shape.}$$

Example 1

The diagram is a sketch of a 'standard' size box of chocolates.

The height of the box is 4.2 cm.
The base OAB is a sector of a circle, centre O.
The radius of the circle is 18 cm and the angle $AOB = 65°$.

Calculate
(a)   the arc length AB.
(b)   the volume of the box.
(c)   the surface area of the box.

An 'economy' size box of chocolates is similar in shape to the 'standard' size box.
The lengths of the 'economy' size box are all 15% greater than the corresponding lengths of the sides of the 'standard' size box.

(d)   Calculate the volume of the 'economy' size box.

Answer

(a)   Using

$$\text{arc } AB = \frac{\pi \times 18 \times 65}{180} = 20.42 \text{ cm } (2 \text{ d.p.})$$

(b)   Volume of box = area of base × height

| volume of prism = area of base × height |

Using **1**

$$\text{Area of sector (base)} = \frac{\pi \times 18^2 \times 65}{360} = 183.78 \text{ cm}^2 (2 \text{ d.p.})$$

So   Volume = $183.78 \times 4.2 = 771.89 \text{ cm}^3$

(c)   Total surface area of box = area of base + area of top + area of
$\qquad$ $OAED$ + area of $OBCD$ + area of curved face $AECB$

Area of base = area of top = 183.78 cm^2 (from (a))

Area of $OAED$ = area of $OBCD = 18 \times 4.2 = 75.6 \text{ cm}^2$

Area of curved surface = arc length AB × height
$\qquad\qquad\qquad = 20.42 \times 4.2 = 85.76 \text{ cm}^2$

So total surface area =
$\qquad 183.78 + 183.78 + 75.6 + 75.6 + 85.76 = 604.52 \text{ cm}^2$

(d)   Length of 'economy' box = 1.15 × length of 'standard'
So the 'standard' box is enlarged by a scale factor of 1.15 to
give the 'economy' size box.

Using **5**
Volume of 'economy' box = 1.15^3 × volume of 'standard' box
$\qquad\qquad\qquad\qquad = 1.15^3 \times 771.89$
$\qquad\qquad\qquad\qquad = 1173.95 \text{ cm}^3$

Worked examination question [E]

A solid metal right circular cone has a height of 12.7 cm and a diameter of 9.4 cm.

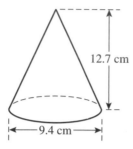

(a)   Calculate the volume of the cone.

The cone is melted down and re-cast as a sphere.
During this process none of the metal is lost.
(b)   Calculate the radius of the sphere.
(c)   Calculate the surface area of the sphere.

Answer

(a)   Using **3**

volume $= \frac{1}{3} \times$ area of base $\times$ height

area of base $= \pi \times 4.7^2$

So   volume $= \frac{1}{3} \times \pi \times 4.7^2 \times 12.7 = 293.78 \, \text{cm}^3$

> area of circle $= \pi r^2$

(b)   Using **4**

volume of sphere $= \frac{4}{3}\pi r^3$

So $\frac{4}{3}\pi r^3 = 293.78$

So $r^3 = \dfrac{3 \times 293.78}{4\pi}$

$= 70.135$

and $r = \sqrt[3]{70.135}$

$= 4.12 \, \text{cm}$

(c)   Using **4**

surface area of sphere $= 4\pi r^2$

$= 4 \times \pi \times 4.12^2$

$= 213.31 \, \text{cm}^2$

Revision exercise 18

1 Two similar boxes have volumes of $2000 \, \text{cm}^3$ and $16\,000 \, \text{cm}^3$.
The area of the base of the larger box is $60 \, \text{cm}^2$.
Calculate the area of the base, in cm^2, of the smaller box.   [E]

2 A rock band festival is to be held in a park.
The diagram represents the part of the park which will be
fenced off to enclose the audience.

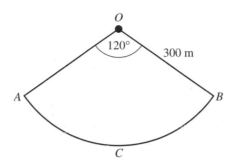

Diagram NOT accurately drawn

OACB is a sector of a circle, centre *O*, radius 300 m.
Angle *AOB* equals 120°.

(a) Calculate the total length of the perimeter of the fence.
Give your answer correct to the nearest 10 metres.

The police are worried about the safety of the audience. They
have said that each person should have at least 3 m² of grass
area.

(b) Calculate the maximum audience allowed to attend the
festival. Give your answer to the nearest 100.

3 A cone has a circular base of diameter 16 cm.
The slant height of the cone is 17 cm.
Calculate the volume of the cone.

4 *VABC* is a tetrahedron. *V* is vertically above *B*.
Angle *ABC* = 90°   *AB* = 9 cm   *BC* = 12 cm
The volume of *VABC* = 360 cm³
Calculate
(a) *VB*   **(b)**   *VA*

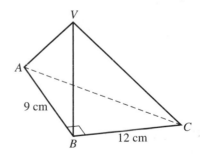

5 The surface area of a sphere is 340 cm³.

Calculate:
(a) the radius of the sphere
(b) the volume of the sphere.

6 *VABCD* is a square-based pyramid.
        AB = 12 cm   *VA* = 20 cm

Calculate the volume of *VABCD*.

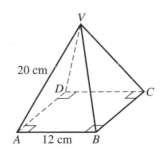

7 *Koke* is sold in two sizes of bottles.
These are called '**standard size**' and '**extra size**'.
The 'standard size' and 'extra size' bottles are similar in shape.

The capacity of a 'standard size' bottle is 1 litre.

The capacity of an 'extra size' bottle is 1.5 litres.

The height of an 'extra size' bottle is 32 cm.

Calculate the height of a 'standard size' bottle.

(A capacity of 1 litre is equivalent to a volume of 1000 cm^3.)

8 The diagram is a sketch of a solid paperweight.
The paperweight consists of a right circular cone on a
hemispherical base.
The diameter of the base of the cone and the diameter of the
hemispherical base are both equal to 8 cm.
The overall height of the paperweight is 14 cm.

Calculate:
(a) the volume of the paperweight
(b) the mass of the paperweight, given that it is made from oak
of density 0.9 g cm^{-3}.

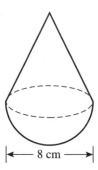

9 The diagram opposite is a sketch of a school javelin arena.
The arena is a sector of a circle, radius 100 m.

Calculate, leaving your answer in terms of π:
(a) the perimeter of the arena
(b) the area of the arena.

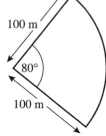

10 A cone has a height of 18 cm and the radius of its base is 3 cm.
(a) Calculate the volume of the cone.

The measurements of the cone are correct to the nearest
millimetre.

(b) Write down the lower bound of the radius of the cone.
(c) Calculate the difference between the upper and lower
bounds of the volume of the cone expressed as a percentage
of the volume of the cone found in part (a).   [E]

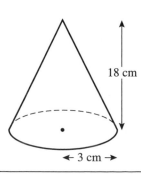

There is more about upper and
lower bounds in Unit 4.

*If your answer is incorrect,
review in the Higher book:*

1 Two containers P and Q are similar.

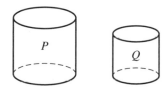

The surface area of container P is 2000 cm^2.
The surface area of container Q is 125 cm^2.
The volume of container P is 4000 cm^3.

Calculate the volume of container Q.   [E, adapted]   *Unit 19, Section 19.3*
Unit 19, Section 19.3

2 There is a light security system.
The system can detect movement inside a sector of a circle.
The radius of the circle is 24 m.
The sector angle is 125°.

Calculate the area of the sector.   [E, adapted]   *Unit 19, Example 3*
Unit 19, Example 3

3 A solid silver rod is in the shape of a cylinder of height 15 cm.
The diameter of its base is 8 cm.
(a) Calculate the volume of the cylinder.   *Unit 19, Example 6*
Unit 19, Example 6

The silver is melted down and re-cast as a solid cone of height
32 cm. During this process none of the silver is lost.

(b) Calculate the radius of the circular base of the cone.   *Unit 19, pages 345–7*
Unit 19, pages 394–6

Answers to Test yourself

1 62.5 cm^3 **2** 628.32 m^2 **3** **(a)** 753.98 cm^3 **(b)** 4.74 cm

19 Vectors

Any quantity, such as velocity or force, which has both magnitude (size) and direction is called a **vector**.

A quantity which has a numerical value only – and can be represented by a number – is called a **scalar**.

Key points to remember

1 A vector can be represented as

$$\begin{pmatrix} x \\ y \end{pmatrix}$$

  or $\overrightarrow{AB}$
  or **a**

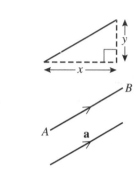

2 The vector *k***a, where** *k is a scalar, is parallel to a and has length*

$$k \times \text{length } \textit{of } a$$

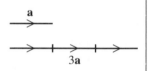

3 **a** + **b** is found by the parallelogram law for addition.

4 **a** − **b** is found by:

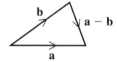

5 The position vector of a point *P is* $\overrightarrow{OP}$*, where O is usually the origin.*

6 If *A and B have position vectors a and b respectively then* **the vector** $\overrightarrow{AB} = \mathbf{b} - \mathbf{a}$

7 If *A and B have position vectors a and b respectively then the position vector of the midpoint, M, of the line joining A to B is*

$$\overrightarrow{OM} = \mathbf{m} = \tfrac{1}{2}(\mathbf{a} + \mathbf{b})$$

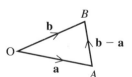

Example 1

ABC is an equilateral triangle.
M is the midpoint of AC.

$$\vec{AB} = \mathbf{a} \qquad \vec{BC} = \mathbf{b}$$

Work out, in terms of a and b, expressions for the vectors:

(i) $\vec{AC}$ (ii) $\vec{MB}$

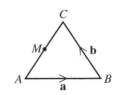

Answer

(i) Using **3**

$$\vec{AC} = \vec{AB} + \vec{BC}$$

So $\qquad \vec{AC} = \mathbf{a} + \mathbf{b}$

(ii) Using **2**

$$AM = \tfrac{1}{2} AC$$

So $\qquad \vec{AM} = \tfrac{1}{2} \vec{AC}$

$$\vec{AM} = \tfrac{1}{2}(\mathbf{a} + \mathbf{b})$$

Using **3**

$$\vec{AM} + \vec{MB} = \vec{AB}$$

So $\qquad \vec{MB} = \vec{AB} - \vec{AM}$

$$\vec{MB} = \mathbf{a} - \tfrac{1}{2}(\mathbf{a} + \mathbf{b}) = \tfrac{1}{2}\mathbf{a} - \tfrac{1}{2}\mathbf{b}$$

$$= \tfrac{1}{2}(\mathbf{a} - \mathbf{b})$$

Worked examination question 1 [E]

$$\vec{PQ} = \begin{pmatrix} 2 \\ 3 \end{pmatrix} \quad \vec{QR} = \begin{pmatrix} 4 \\ 5 \end{pmatrix} \quad \vec{TS} = \begin{pmatrix} 3 \\ 4 \end{pmatrix}$$

(a) Show that *PR is parallel to TS*.
(b) Write down the ratio of the length of *PR to the length of TS*.

Answer

(a) Using **3**

$$\vec{PR} = \vec{PQ} + \vec{QR}$$

$$= \begin{pmatrix} 2 \\ 3 \end{pmatrix} + \begin{pmatrix} 4 \\ 5 \end{pmatrix} = \begin{pmatrix} 6 \\ 8 \end{pmatrix} = 2\begin{pmatrix} 3 \\ 4 \end{pmatrix}$$

$$\vec{PR} = 2\vec{TS}$$

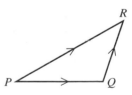

So from **2**

$\qquad$ *PR is parallel to TS*

(b) Using **2**

$\qquad$ **length of** $PR = 2 \times$ **length of** *TS*

or $\qquad$ length PR : length $TS = 2 : 1$

Worked examination question 2 [E]

ABCDE is a regular pentagon.
$$\overrightarrow{AB} = \mathbf{p}, \quad \overrightarrow{BC} = \mathbf{q}, \quad \overrightarrow{CD} = \mathbf{r}$$
(a)   In terms of p, q and r, find expressions for
   (i) $\overrightarrow{AC}$ (ii) $\overrightarrow{AD}$

M is the point on AD such that $DM = \frac{1}{3}DA$.
(b)   Find expressions for
   (i) $\overrightarrow{AM}$ **(ii)** $\overrightarrow{MC}$

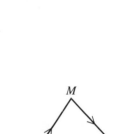

Answer

(a)   (i)   Using **3**
$$\overrightarrow{AC} = \overrightarrow{AB} + \overrightarrow{BC}$$
So
$$\overrightarrow{AC} = \mathbf{p} + \mathbf{q}$$
   (ii)   Using **3** again
$$\overrightarrow{AD} = \overrightarrow{AB} + \overrightarrow{BC} + \overrightarrow{CD}$$
$$\overrightarrow{AD} = \mathbf{p} + \mathbf{q} + \mathbf{r}$$
(b)   (i)
$$DM = \tfrac{1}{3}DA$$
   So $AM = \tfrac{2}{3}AD$

   Using 2
$$\overrightarrow{AM} = \tfrac{2}{3}\overrightarrow{AD}$$
$$= \tfrac{2}{3}(\mathbf{p} + \mathbf{q} + \mathbf{r})$$
   (ii)   Using **3**
$$\overrightarrow{AM} + \overrightarrow{MC} = \overrightarrow{AC}$$
$$\overrightarrow{MC} = \overrightarrow{AC} - \overrightarrow{AM}$$
   so
$$MC = (\mathbf{p} + \mathbf{q}) - \tfrac{2}{3}(\mathbf{p} + \mathbf{q} + \mathbf{r})$$
$$= \mathbf{p} + \mathbf{q} - \tfrac{2}{3}\mathbf{p} - \tfrac{2}{3}\mathbf{q} - \tfrac{2}{3}\mathbf{r}$$
$$= \tfrac{1}{3}\mathbf{p} + \tfrac{1}{3}\mathbf{q} - \tfrac{2}{3}\mathbf{r}$$

Revision exercise 19

1 The vectors $\overrightarrow{OP}$ and $\overrightarrow{OQ}$ are given by
$$\overrightarrow{OP} = \begin{pmatrix} 3 \\ 2 \end{pmatrix} \quad \text{and} \quad \overrightarrow{OQ} = \begin{pmatrix} 2 \\ -1 \end{pmatrix}$$
   (a) Draw the vectors $\overrightarrow{OP}$ and $\overrightarrow{OQ}$ on a grid.
   (b) Find the vector
$$\overrightarrow{OP} + \overrightarrow{OQ}$$
   and draw it on your grid.
   (c) Find the vector $\overrightarrow{OP} - \overrightarrow{OQ}$ [E]

2 $\mathbf{a} = \begin{pmatrix} -2 \\ 4 \end{pmatrix}$ $\mathbf{b} = \begin{pmatrix} 3 \\ 2 \end{pmatrix}$ $\mathbf{c} = \begin{pmatrix} 5 \\ 6 \end{pmatrix}$

Show that $\mathbf{a} + 4\mathbf{b}$ is parallel to c.

3 *A is the point with coordinates $(2, 5)$.*
B is the point with coordinates $(6, 7)$.
M is the midpoint of AB
O is the origin.
Work out the position vector $\overrightarrow{OM}$.

4 *ABC is a triangle*
$$AB = \mathbf{a}, \quad BC = \mathbf{b}$$
(a) Find an expression, in terms of a and b for AC.

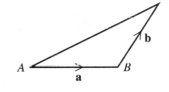

P is the point on AB such that $AP = \frac{2}{3}AB$.
Q is the point on AC such that
$$AQ : QC = 2 : 3$$
(b) Find an expression in terms of a and b for $\overrightarrow{PQ}$.
(c) Explain whether or not PQ is parallel to BC.

5 In the diagram
$$AB = 3AS, \quad BT = \tfrac{1}{2}BC, \quad SC = 4SX$$
$$\overrightarrow{AS} = \mathbf{a}, \ \overrightarrow{BT} = \mathbf{b}$$
Find, in terms of **a** and **b**, expressions for
(a) $\overrightarrow{SB}$ **(b)** $\overrightarrow{AT}$ **(c)** $\overrightarrow{SC}$ **(d)** $\overrightarrow{AX}$

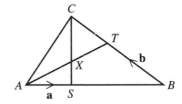

6 The diagram shows a triangle ABC.
P is the midpoint of AB and Q is the point on AC such that
$QC = 2AQ$.

$$\overrightarrow{AP} = \mathbf{x} \ \text{and} \ \overrightarrow{AQ} = \mathbf{y}$$

(a) Write $\overrightarrow{PQ}$ in terms of x and y.
T is a point such that $\overrightarrow{AT} = \overrightarrow{BC}$.
(b) Show that PQT is a straight line *[E]*

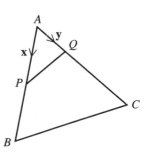

7 In the diagram, Q is the midpoint of the side PR and T is the midpoint of the side PS of the triangle PRS.

$$\overrightarrow{PQ} = \mathbf{a}, \quad \overrightarrow{PT} = \mathbf{b}$$

(a) Write down, in terms of **a** and **b**, the vectors
   (i) $\overrightarrow{QT}$ (ii) $\overrightarrow{PR}$ (iii) $\overrightarrow{RS}$
(b) Write down one geometrical fact about QT and RS which
   could be deduced from your answers to part **(a)** *[E]*

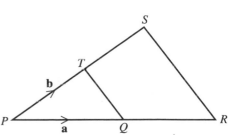

If your answer is incorrect, review in the Higher book:

1 $\overrightarrow{OP} = \begin{pmatrix} -3 \\ 4 \end{pmatrix}$; $\overrightarrow{OR} = \begin{pmatrix} 5 \\ 6 \end{pmatrix}$

and *M is the midpoint of PR.*

(a) Find $\overrightarrow{PR}$ *Unit 26, Examples 7 and 8*
                                                   Unit 25, Examples 7 and 8

(b) Find $\overrightarrow{OM}$ *Unit 26, Examples 8 and 9*
                                                   Unit 25, Examples 8 and 9

(c) Find the vector $\overrightarrow{OQ}$ such that *OPQR is a parallelogram.*   *Unit 26, Section 26.6*
                                                   Unit 25, Section 25.6

---

2 *ABCD is a trapezium.*
DC is a parallel to AB.
        $DC = 3AB$

ABPQ is a parallelogram
        $\overrightarrow{AB} = \mathbf{a}$, $\overrightarrow{AD} = \mathbf{b}$, $\overrightarrow{AQ} = \mathbf{c}$

In terms of a, b and c, find expressions for:
(a) vector $\overrightarrow{DC}$ *Unit 26, Section 26.5*
                                                   Unit 25, Section 25.5

(b) vector $\overrightarrow{AC}$ *Unit 26, Section 26.5*
                                                   Unit 25, Section 25.5

(c) vector $\overrightarrow{BC}$ *Unit 26, Section 26.5*
                                                   Unit 25, Section 25.5

(d) vector $\overrightarrow{PC}$ *Unit 26, Section 26.5*
                                                   Unit 25, Section 25.5

Answers to Test yourself

1 (a) $\begin{pmatrix} 8 \\ 2 \end{pmatrix}$ (b) $\begin{pmatrix} 1 \\ 5 \end{pmatrix}$ (c) $\begin{pmatrix} 2 \\ 10 \end{pmatrix}$ 2 (a) 3a   (b) b + 3a   (c) b + 2a   (d) b + 2a − c

20 Circle theorems

You should know and be able to use each of these theorems.

Key points to remember

1 The perpendicular bisector of any chord passes through the centre of the circle.

2 The angle between a tangent and a radius is 90°.

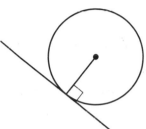

3 The lengths of the two tangents from a point are equal.
For example, $PT = PS$

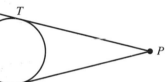

4 The angle in a semicircle is always a right angle.

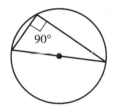

5 The angle at the centre is twice the angle at the circumference, for example:
$$A\hat{O}B = 2 \times A\hat{C}B$$

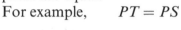

6 Angles in the same segment are equal, for example:
$$A\hat{C}B = A\hat{D}B$$

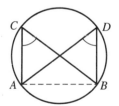

7 Opposite angles of a cyclic quadrilateral are supplementary.
For example,
$$x + y = 180°$$

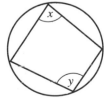

8 The angle between a tangent and its chord is equal to the angle in the alternate segment. For example,
$$a = b$$

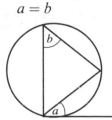

This is called the alternate segment theorem.

Example 1

PT is a tangent to the circle, centre *O*.
Angle $T\hat{O}B = 110°$

Calculate the angle *BTP*.
Give reasons for your calculation.

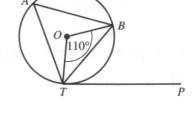

Answer

Using **8**

> angle *BTP* = angle *BAT* (alternate segment)

Also, using **5**

> angle $BAT = \frac{1}{2}$ of angle *TOB* (angle at centre)

So   angle $BAT = \frac{1}{2}$ of 110°

> $= 55°$

so   angle $BTP = 55°$

Worked examination question [E]

The line *ABC* is a tangent to the circle at *B*.
Angle $FBD = 85°$ and angle $BEF = 31°$

Calculate the size of angle *ABD*.
Give reasons for your calculation.
Show all steps in your working.
You may get some credit for finding any angle in the diagram
provided you give a reason.

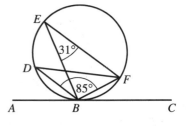

Answer

Using **8**

> angle *FBC* = angle *BEF* (alternate segment)

So   angle $FBC = 31°$

Also   angle *ABD* + angle *FBD* + angle *FBC* = 180° (straight line)
So   angle $ABD + 85° + 31° = 180°$
                angle $ABD + 116° = 180°$
                angle $ABD = 64°$

Revision exercise 20

1 In the diagram, *SU* is a diameter of the circle centre *O*.
PT is a tangent to the circle at *T*.
QST and *QVU* are straight lines.
Angle $STP = 56°$
Angle $SQV = 17°$

Find the size of angle *VUS*.

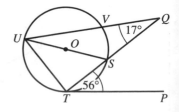

2 AB is a tangent to a circle, centre O,
Angle $BOD = 124°$
Angle $CDB = 31°$

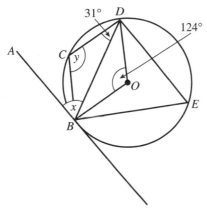

Calculate the sizes of the angles marked x and y.

3 Points A, B, C and D lie on the circumference of a circle.
TC is a tangent.
AD is parallel to BC.
Angle $BAD = 85°$
Angle $TCD = 47°$

Calculate the angles marked
(a) x **(b)** y

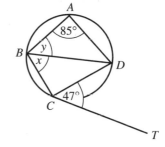

4 $ABCD$ is a cyclic quadrilateral.
The line PAQ is a tangent at A to the circle.
AB extended meets DC extended at the point X.
$BD = BX$
Angle $DAQ = 48°$
Angle $XCB = 70°$

Giving your reasons, find the sizes of the angles:
(a) $A\hat{B}D$ **(b)** $B\hat{A}D$ **(c)** $X\hat{B}D$ **(d)** $C\hat{D}B$

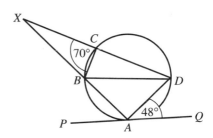

5 BC, AB and AC are tangents to the circle at D, E and F
respectively.
The angle $EBD = x°$
The angle $FCD = y°$

Giving your reasons, find an expression in x and y for the angle
EDF.

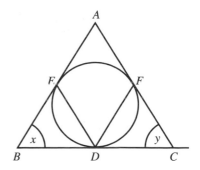

6 The points B, C and D lie on a circle centre O.
Angle $DCB = x°$. AB is a tangent to the circle.
  (a) Write down an expression for angle DOB.
  (b) Without quoting the alternate segment theorem, prove that:
  angle $ABD = x°$

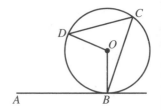

7 TP and TQ are tangents from T to the circle, centre O.
  (a) Explain why it is possible to draw a circle which passes
  through all four of the points O, P, T and Q.

Angle $PTQ = 50°$, $OP = 12$ cm.
  (b) Calculate the length of the radius of the circle through
  $OPTQ$.
  Give your answer to the nearest millimetre.

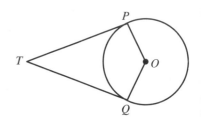

Test yourself	**What to review**

1 $ABCD$ and E lie on the circumference of a circle centre O.
COE is a diameter of the circle.
PA is a tangent to the circle at A.
$CD = ED$
Angle $EAP = 36°$

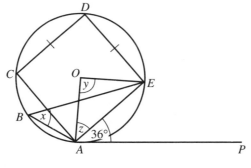

Find:

(a) angle x

(b) angle y

(c) angle z

*If your answer is incorrect,
review in the Higher book:*

Unit 28, Section 28.6
Unit 26, Section 26.6

Unit 28, Section 28.3
Unit 26, Section 26.3

Unit 28, Example 3
Unit 26, Example 3

Answers to test yourself

1   (a) $x = 36°$ (b) $y = 72°$ (c) $z = 54°$

21 Sampling

Sampling techniques are used to collect statistics when it is unrealistic to obtain the views of an entire population or test all of the components being manufactured.

Key points to remember

1 A random sample is one in which each member of the population is equally likely to be selected.

2 A stratified sample is one in which the population is divided into groups called strata and each stratum is randomly sampled.

3 A selective sample is one in which every nth item is chosen, where n is selected at random.

Example 1

There are 1200 pupils at Marriott School.
660 of the pupils are girls.
540 of the pupils are boys.

The Headteacher of the school, Mrs Lukin, wishes to find out if the pupils would like her to set up a 'School Council' which has pupil representation.

Mrs Lukin decides to take a sample of the views of the pupils. She needs to have information about the views of the girls and the boys.

Mrs Lukin has time to interview 50 pupils to obtain their views.

Explain how Mrs Lukin could design a sampling method to obtain the views of the girls and boys at her school.

Answer

The population of the school is divided into two groups – girls and boys. Using **2**, Mrs Lukin needs to use a stratified sampling technique.

Of the pupils at the school, 660 are girls, so the proportion of girls is:

$$\frac{660}{1200} = 0.55$$

So in the 50 pupils she interviews there should be:
$$0.55 \times 50 = 27.5 \text{ girls}$$
and $$50 - 27.5 = 22.5 \text{ boys}$$

She cannot interview 0.5 of a pupil, so she should toss a coin to decide whether to interview
either 28 girls and 22 boys
or 27 girls and 23 boys.

Once she has decided on (say) 28 girls, she could take a random sample of 28 out of the 660 girls. One way of doing so could be to put all 660 girls' names in a hat and select 28 of them – without looking.

Then she could repeat this process with the boys' names, but selecting only 22 names.

Worked examination question [E]

There are 200 members of the Martineau Golf Club.
Their age ranges and gender are given in the table below.

Age (*a*) years	Frequency	
	Male	Female
$0 \leqslant a < 20$	20	10
$20 \leqslant a < 40$	48	34
$40 \leqslant a < 60$	42	28
$60 \leqslant a < 80$	12	6

The club captain decides to conduct a survey of the members, in order to obtain their views about the building of a new club house. He wishes his sample size to be about 50 of the club members and to take account of their ages and gender.

(a) How many males should there be in the sample?
Give your answer correct to the nearest whole number.

(b) How many of the sample should be aged under 40 years?
Give your answer correct to the nearest whole number.

(c) How many of the sample should be females aged between 20 years and 40 years?
Give your answer correct to the nearest whole number.

Answer

As a fraction, or decimal, of the total number of members, the 50 to be sampled is

$$\frac{50}{200} = \frac{1}{4} \text{ or } 0.25$$

(a) Using **2** the stratum of males has a total of
$$20 + 48 + 42 + 12 = 122$$
So there need to be
$$0.25 \times 122 = 30.5$$
30 or 31 males should be included in the sample.

(b) Using **2** the stratum of members aged under 40 has a total of
$$20 + 10 + 48 + 34 = 112$$
So there need to be
$$0.25 \times 112 = 28$$
28 members in the sample should be under 40.

(c) Using **2** the stratum of females aged between 20 and 40 has a
total of 34.
So there need to be
$$0.25 \times 34 = 8.5$$
8 or 9 females aged between 20 and 40 should be included in the
sample.

Example 2

Explain how to take a selective sample of 4% of electrical
components from a production line.

Answer

$$4\% = \frac{4}{100} = \frac{1}{25}$$

To take a 4% sample you select 1 in every 25 items and test them.
Choose a number at random between 1 and 25 – say it is n.
Then, using **3** sample the nth, $(n + 25)$th, $(n + 50)$th, ..., etc
component from the production line.

Revision exercise 21

1 There are 1600 pupils at Manor High School.
The table shows how these pupils are distributed by year group
and gender.

Year group	Number of boys	Number of girls
7	158	164
8	149	162
9	171	158
10	160	162
11	162	154

Joan is conducting a survey about pupils' favourite hobbies.
She decides to use a stratified random sample of 200 pupils
according to year group and gender.

(a) How many year 11 girls should there be in her sample?
(b) How many year 8 boys should there be in her sample?

2 Explain how to take a selective sample of 5% of the 1200 pupils at Lucea High School.

3 There are 40 000 people who can vote in an election. They are categorised according to age and gender as in the table below.

Age range (years)	Number of males	Number of females
Under 35	7800	8300
35 or over	12 600	11 300

Just before the election, a market research company makes a survey of the voting intentions of these people. They will try to obtain the views of 2400 people.

Work out the number in the sample who should be
(a) female aged under 35   **(b)** male   **(c)** aged 35 or over.

Test yourself

What to review

1 There are 12 000 students at Lucea College.

The table shows how the students are distributed by type of course and gender.

If your answer is incorrect, review in the Higher book:

Course type	Number of males	Number of females
Full-time	2400	2600
Part-time	3800	3200

The college management team decide to obtain the views of the students on a proposed new car-parking scheme.

Describe how the management team could take a sample of 240 students so that it will be representative of the views of male, female, full-time and part-time students.

Unit 4, page 70
Unit 4, page 75

2 Explain how you could take a selective sample of 10% of the names from an electoral register.

Unit 4, page 71
Unit 4, page 76

Answers to Test yourself

1 Stratified sample with numbers as below:

Course type	Male	Female
full-time	48	52
part-time	76	64

2 Take a random number from 1 to 10 – call it *n*. Then sample *n*th, $(n + 10)$th, $(n + 20)$th, etc. names.

22 Mean for frequency tables

Sometimes discrete or continuous data is grouped into class intervals. You can estimate the mean from grouped data.

Key points to remember

1 An estimate of the mean for grouped data is:

$$\bar{x} = \frac{\Sigma fx}{\Sigma f}$$

where x is the midpoint of each class interval and f is the frequency.

2 To draw a frequency polygon, you plot the frequency against the midpoint of each class interval and join the points with straight lines.

Worked examination question [E]

The grouped frequency table gives information about the weekly rainfall (d) in millimetres at Heathrow Airport in 1995.

Weekly rainfall (d) in mm	Number of weeks
$0 \leqslant d < 10$	20
$10 \leqslant d < 20$	18
$20 \leqslant d < 30$	6
$30 \leqslant d < 40$	4
$40 \leqslant d < 50$	2
$50 \leqslant d < 60$	2

(a) Calculate an estimate for the mean weekly rainfall.
(b) Draw the frequency polygon for this information.

Answer

(a) Using **1** we find the midpoints of each class interval (the x column) and multiply these by the frequency for each interval.

Weekly rainfall (d) in mm	Number of weeks (f)	Midpoint x	fx
$0 \leqslant d < 10$	20	5	100
$10 \leqslant d < 20$	18	15	270
$20 \leqslant d < 30$	6	25	150
$30 \leqslant d < 40$	4	35	140
$40 \leqslant d < 50$	2	45	90
$50 \leqslant d < 60$	2	55	110
	Total $\Sigma f = 52$		Total $\Sigma fx = 860$

Estimate of mean $= \dfrac{\Sigma fx}{\Sigma f} = \dfrac{860}{52} = 16.54\,\text{mm}$

(b)   Using **2** the frequency polygon is:

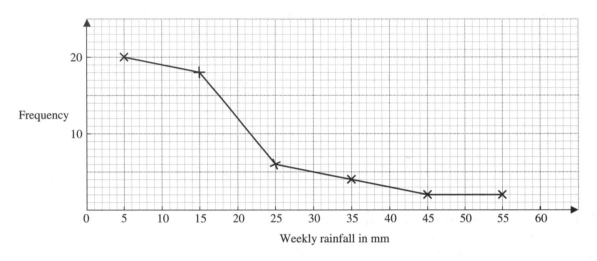

Weekly rainfall in mm

Revision exercise 22

1   Bronwen owns a pet shop.
The table gives information about the
weights of hamsters in Bronwen's shop.

Calculate an estimate for the mean weight
of the hamsters in Bronwen's shop.

Weight w of hamster in grams	Number of hamsters
$28 \leqslant w < 30$	9
$30 \leqslant w < 32$	5
$32 \leqslant w < 34$	4
$34 \leqslant w < 36$	2

2   A survey was carried out in Mathstown
High School to find out how long it takes
the pupils to travel to school.

The results of the survey are shown in the
table.

(a) Write down the modal interval for the
pupils.
(b) Work out an estimate for the mean
time taken for the pupils to travel to
school.
(c) Draw a frequency polygon for this
information.   [E]

Time, t minutes, to travel to school	Number of pupils
$0 < t \leqslant 10$	14
$10 < t \leqslant 20$	12
$20 < t \leqslant 30$	19
$30 < t \leqslant 40$	5
Total	50

Remember the mode is the most
frequent value.

3 A bag contains 20 potatoes. The weights of these potatoes are shown in the frequency table.

Work out an estimate for the mean weight of the potatoes in the bag.

Weight (w) grams	Frequency
$100 < w \leqslant 200$	4
$200 < w \leqslant 300$	6
$300 < w \leqslant 400$	9
$400 < w \leqslant 500$	1

4 A survey was carried out to find out how much time was needed by a group of pupils to complete homework set on a particular monday evening. The results are shown in the table below.

Calculate an estimate for the mean time spent on homework by the pupils in the group.   [E]

Time, t hours, spent on homework	Number of pupils
0	3
$0 < t \leqslant 1$	14
$1 < t \leqslant 2$	17
$2 < t \leqslant 3$	5
$3 < t \leqslant 4$	1

Test yourself   What to review

1 The table shows the frequency distribution of marks scored by 100 candidates in a Science examination.

(a) Calculate an estimate of the mean mark.

(b) Draw a frequency polygon to illustrate the data.

Marks	Frequency
0–9	3
10–19	5
20–29	12
30–39	20
40–49	24
50–59	18
60–69	12
70–79	6

If your answer is incorrect, review in the Higher book:

Unit 15, Example 3
Unit 15, Example 3

Unit 4, Section 4.7
Unit 4, Section 4.7

Answers to Test yourself

1 (a) 43.4   (b)

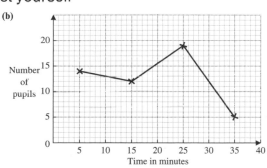

23 Cumulative frequency curves

The cumulative frequency curve is used to estimate the median, some measures of spread and various proportions for data in a grouped frequency table or distribution.

Key points to remember

1 The median is the middle value of the distribution.

2 The lower quartile is the value one quarter of the way into the distribution.

3 The upper quartile is the value three quarters of the way into the distribution.

4 Interquartile range
= upper quartile − lower quartile

5 The cumulative frequency curve can be used to find the percentage or proportion of the whole distribution lying between two values.

6 To compare two distributions you should use a measure of average and a measure of spread.

7 A box and whisker diagram, or box plot, is a visual way of representing the median and the interquartile range.

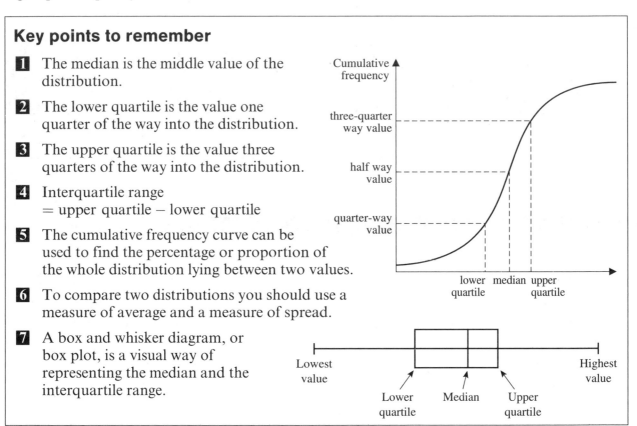

Example 1
Lucea Golf Club has 200 members.
The ages of the members are grouped and set out in the table below.

Age (*a* years)	Frequency
$0 \leqslant a < 10$	8
$10 \leqslant a < 20$	26
$20 \leqslant a < 30$	32
$30 \leqslant a < 40$	45
$40 \leqslant a < 50$	37
$50 \leqslant a < 60$	29
$60 \leqslant a < 70$	16
$70 \leqslant a < 80$	7

(a) Construct a cumulative frequency table.
(b) Draw the cumulative frequency curve.
(c) Work out an estimate of the median.
(d) Work out the interquartile range.
(e) Draw the box plot for the distribution.
(f) Estimate the percentage of members aged between 35 years and 55 years.

The median age of the members of Russell Golf Club is 42 years.
The interquartile range of the members of Russell Golf Club is 33 years.

(g) Compare the distribution of members' ages of the two golf clubs.

Answer

(a) The cumulative frequency table is

Age	Cumulative frequency
$a < 10$	8
$a < 20$	$8 + 26 = 34$
$a < 30$	$34 + 32 = 66$ (etc)
$a < 40$	111
$a < 50$	148
$a < 60$	177
$a < 70$	193
$a < 80$	200

(b) The cumulative frequency curve is:

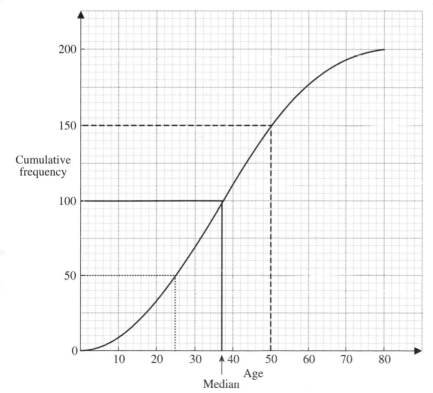

Plot the cumulative frequencies against the upper class boundaries.

(c) Using **1** the median is found from the solid lines on the graph.
The estimated median = 37 years

(d) Using **2** the lower quartile is found from the dotted lines on the graph.
The estimated lower quartile = 25 years
Using **3** the upper quartile is found from the dashed lines on the graph.
The estimated upper quartile = 50 years
Using **4**
$$\text{interquartile range} = 50 - 25 = 25 \text{ years}$$

(e) We cannot be sure about the positions of the box for Russell, but it is wider than the box for Lucea.

(f) Using **5** on a new copy of the cumulative frequency graph, the estimated number of members between 35 years and 55 years is shown by the two dashed lines.

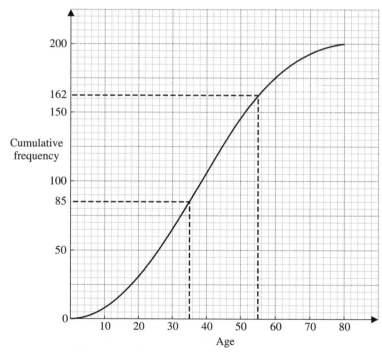

The estimate is
$$162 - 85 = 77 \text{ members}$$
As a percentage, 77 out of 200 is
$$\frac{77}{200} = 38.5\%$$

(g) Using **6**
Comparing the medians:
median age for Russell > median age for Lucea
so it might appear that, on the whole, the Lucea members are younger than the Russell members.

However,
interquartile range at Russell >
interquartile range at Lucea
This means that the ages of members
at Russell are more widely spread than
at Lucea. So there could be many
members at Russell who are much
younger than the members at Lucea.

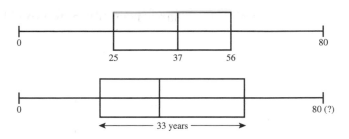

Revision exercise 23

1 The grouped frequency table gives information about the
weekly rainfall (d) in millimetres at Heathrow Airport in 1995.

Weekly rainfall (d) in mm	Number of weeks
$0 \leqslant d < 10$	20
$10 \leqslant d < 20$	18
$20 \leqslant d < 30$	6
$30 \leqslant d < 40$	4
$40 \leqslant d < 50$	2
$50 \leqslant d < 60$	2

(a) Construct a cumulative frequency table.
(b) Draw the cumulative frequency curve.
(c) Estimate the median weekly rainfall.
(d) Estimate the interquartile range for the rainfall.
(e) Draw the box plot for the distribution.
(f) Estimate the number of weeks in which the rainfall was less
than 15 mm.   [E]

2 The table gives information about the weights of 100 newborn
babies.

Weight (w) in kg	Frequency
$1.0 \leqslant w < 1.5$	4
$1.5 \leqslant w < 2.0$	9
$2.0 \leqslant w < 2.5$	11
$2.5 \leqslant w < 3.0$	21
$3.0 \leqslant w < 3.5$	26
$3.5 \leqslant w < 4.0$	18
$4.0 \leqslant w < 4.5$	9
$4.5 \leqslant w < 5.0$	2

(a) Construct a cumulative frequency table.
(b) Draw a cumulative frequency graph for your table.
(c) Use your cumulative frequency diagram to estimate the median weight, in kilograms, of the newborn babies. Show your method clearly.
(d) Work out an estimate for the interquartile range of the weights of the newborn babies and draw the box plot for their distribution.
(e) Estimate the percentage of babies born with a weight between 2.2 kg and 3.6 kg. [E]

3 The grouped frequency table shows the distribution of the amounts of daily sunshine, in hours, in Downtown in August 1997.

(a) Construct a cumulative frequency table.
(b) Draw the cumulative frequency graph.
(c) Use your cumulative frequency graph to find an estimate for the median amount of daily sunshine, in hours, in August 1997.
Make your method clear.
(d) Estimate the interquartile range for the hours of sunshine in Downtown in August 1997.

Amounts (s) of daily sunshine in hours	Number of days in this class interval
$0 \leqslant s < 2$	2
$2 \leqslant s < 4$	1
$4 \leqslant s < 6$	3
$6 \leqslant s < 8$	8
$8 \leqslant s < 10$	11
$10 \leqslant s < 12$	4
$12 \leqslant s < 14$	2

In Ashwell during August 1997, the median number of hours of daily sunshine was 10.2 hours and the interquartile range was 3 hours.

(e) Compare the distributions of hours of daily sunshine in Downtown and Ashwell for August 1997.

4 A large company is considering paying travelling expenses to its employees who work extra days. To find out how much it is likely to cost the company, a survey was carried out on costs of travel. The results are analysed below.

Cost of travel to and from work

£1 or less	10 employees
more than £1 but no more than £2	20 employees
more than £2 but no more than £3	35 employees
more than £3 but no more than £4	25 employees
more than £4 but no more than £5	8 employees
more than £5 but no more than £6	2 employees
more than £6	0 employees
	100

(a) Copy and complete the cumulative frequency table opposite.
(b) Draw the cumulative frequency curve.
(c) Use your graph to estimate
  (i) the median cost of travel
 (ii) the lower quartile cost of travel
(iii) the upper quartile cost of travel
(iv) the percentage of employees who spent more than £3.70 on their travel. [E]

Cost, £c, of travel	Cumulative frequency
$c \leqslant 1$	
$c \leqslant 2$	
$c \leqslant 3$	
$c \leqslant 4$	
$c \leqslant 5$	
$c \leqslant 6$	

| **Test yourself** | **What to review** |

1 The table shows the battery life, t minutes, of a sample of 80 Omega batteries.

If your answer is incorrect, review in the Higher book:

Battery life (in minutes)	**Number of batteries (frequency)**
$t < 280$	0
$280 \leqslant t < 290$	5
$290 \leqslant t < 300$	9
$300 \leqslant t < 310$	10
$310 \leqslant t < 320$	15
$320 \leqslant t < 330$	17
$330 \leqslant t < 340$	12
$340 \leqslant t < 350$	8
$350 \leqslant t < 360$	4

(a) Form a cumulative frequency table.

Unit 4, Section 4.8
Unit 4, Section 4.8

(b) Draw the cumulative frequency curve.

Unit 4, pages 75–79
Unit 4, pages 80–84

(c) Estimate the median battery life.

Unit 15, page 277
Unit 15, page 318

(d) Estimate the interquartile range of the battery lives.

Unit 15, pages 278–80
Unit 15, pages 318–321

(e) Draw the box plot for the distribution.

A shop owner buys a box of 720 Omega batteries.
(f) Use your graph to estimate how many of these batteries will have a battery life of between 315 and 345 minutes. Show your method clearly.   [E]

Unit 15, Section 15.5
Unit 15, Section 15.5

Answers to Test yourself

1 (a)

Battery life	Cumulative frequency
$t < 280$	0
$t < 290$	5
$t < 300$	14
$t < 310$	24
$t < 320$	39
$t < 330$	56
$t < 340$	68
$t < 350$	76
$t < 360$	80

(b)

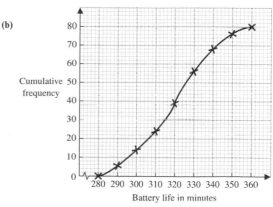

(c) Just over 320 h   **(d)** About 27 h

(e)

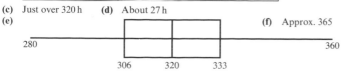

(f) Approx. 365

24 Histograms and moving averages

A histogram is a way of representing data from a frequency table.
A moving average is a way of presenting data to smooth out
seasonal variations.

Key points to remember

1 A histogram can be drawn for equal class intervals.

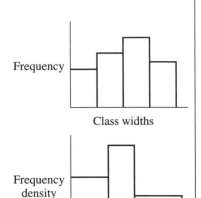

2 A histogram can be drawn for unequal class intervals.

3 When unequal class intervals are used the vertical axis is
frequency density.

4 Frequency density $= \dfrac{\text{frequency}}{\text{class width}}$

5 For any histogram the areas of the rectangles are
proportional to the frequencies they represent.

6 For a set of data as

$x_1, x_2, x_3, x_4, x_5, x_6, x_7 \ldots$

the four-point moving averages are

$$\frac{x_1 + x_2 + x_3 + x_4}{4}, \frac{x_2 + x_3 + x_4 + x_5}{4}, \frac{x_3 + x_4 + x_5 + x_6}{4}, \ldots$$

7 Moving averages can be plotted to show overall trends in
time series.

Time series

Time series with moving
averages and overall
'trend' line

Example 1

A sack contains 108 potatoes.
The frequency table gives information about the masses of these potatoes.

Mass (m) grams	Frequency
$0 < m \leqslant 100$	7
$100 < m \leqslant 150$	26
$150 < m \leqslant 200$	30
$200 < m \leqslant 250$	35
$250 < m \leqslant 400$	10

Use the information to draw the histogram for this distribution.

Answer

Using **3** and **4** work out the frequency density using

$$\text{frequency density} = \frac{\text{frequency}}{\text{class width}}$$

Mass	Frequency	Class width	Frequency density
0 to 100	7	100	$7 \div 100 = 0.07$
100 to 150	26	50	$26 \div 50 = 0.52$
150 to 200	30	50	$30 \div 50 = 0.6$
200 to 250	35	50	$35 \div 50 = 0.7$
250 to 400	12	150	$12 \div 150 = 0.08$

Now draw the histogram, using **2** and **4**

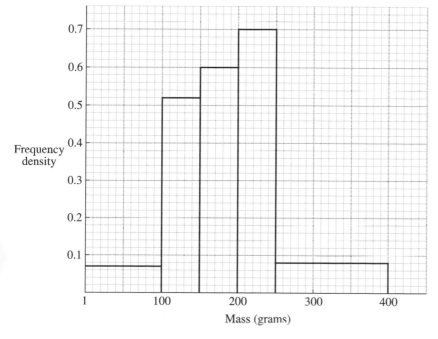

Worked examination question 1 [E]

The histogram gives information about the ages of the teachers at a school on 1st September last year.

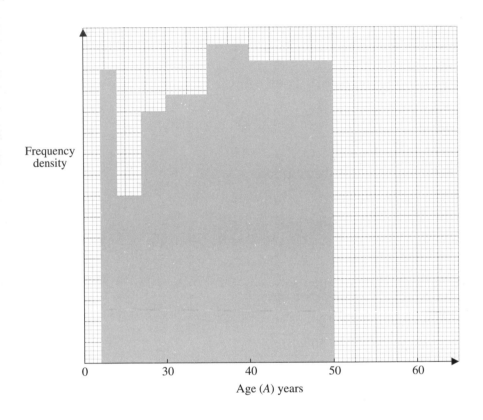

Age (A) years

(a) Use the information in the histogram to complete the frequency table.

Age (A) years	Frequency
$22 \leqslant A < 24$	
$24 \leqslant A < 27$	
$27 \leqslant A < 30$	
$30 \leqslant A < 35$	16
$35 \leqslant A < 40$	19
$40 \leqslant A < 50$	
$50 \leqslant A < 65$	27

(b) Use the information in the frequency table to complete the histogram.

Answer

(a) For the 30 to 35 age group, using ▉**4**

$$\text{frequency density} = \frac{\text{frequency}}{\text{class width}} = \frac{16}{5} = 3.2$$

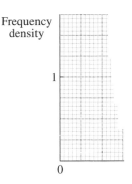

So, on the grid, 64 squares represent 3.2 units

∴   20 squares represent 1   unit

So the scale for the frequency density axis is as shown, right.

Now work out the frequency densities (heights of bars) for each age range using ▉**4** again:

$$\text{frequency} = \text{frequency density} \times \text{class width}$$

Age range	Frequency density	Class width	Frequency
22 to 24	3.5	2	7
24 to 27	2	3	6
27 to 30	3	3	9
30 to 35	3.2	5	16
35 to 40	3.8	5	19
40 to 50	3.6	10	36
50 to 65	$\frac{27}{15} = 1.8$	15	27

(b) Using ▉**5** the completed histogram is:

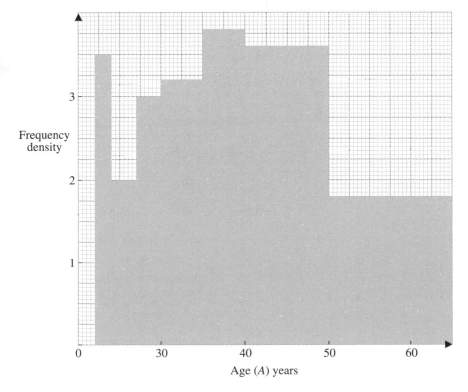

Age (A) years

Example 2

Gemma has the following information about the gas bills for her home over the period from 1996 to 2000 inclusive.

	1st quarter	2nd quarter	3rd quarter	4th quarter
1996	180	92	40	140
1997	206	100	45	152
1998	214	108	50	164
1999	220	118	56	170
2000	232	126	62	180

(a)   Plot the quartely gas bills as a time series.
(b)   Work out the four-point moving averages for these gas bills.
(c)   On the same axes as the quarterly gas bills, plot the moving averages.
(d)   Comment on the changes in the gas bill at Gemma's house between 1996 and 2000.

Answer

(a)

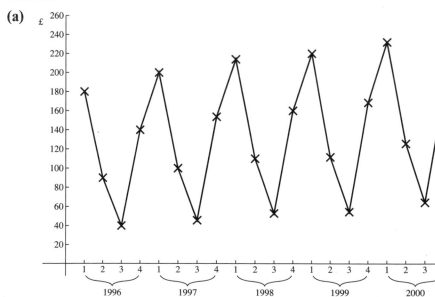

(b)   The four-part moving averages are:

$$\frac{180 + 92 + 40 + 140}{4} = 113$$

$$\frac{92 + 40 + 140 + 206}{4} = 119.5$$

$$\frac{40 + 140 + 206 + 100}{4} = 121.5$$

Note:
To go from

$$\frac{180 + 92 + 40 + 140}{4}(=113)$$

to

$$\frac{92 + 40 + 140 + 206}{4}$$

the top row has been increased by $206 - 180 = 26$.

$$\frac{26}{4} = 6.5$$

so the moving average increases by 6.5 to 119.5.

$$\frac{140 + 206 + 100 + 45}{4} = 122.75 \qquad \frac{50 + 164 + 220 + 118}{4} = 138$$

$$\frac{206 + 100 + 45 + 152}{4} = 125.75 \qquad \frac{164 + 220 + 118 + 56}{4} = 139.5$$

$$\frac{100 + 45 + 152 + 214}{4} = 127.75 \qquad \frac{220 + 118 + 56 + 170}{4} = 141$$

$$\frac{45 + 152 + 214 + 108}{4} = 129.75 \qquad \frac{118 + 56 + 170 + 232}{4} = 144$$

$$\frac{152 + 214 + 108 + 50}{4} = 131 \qquad \frac{56 + 170 + 232 + 126}{4} = 146$$

$$\frac{214 + 108 + 50 + 164}{4} = 134 \qquad \frac{170 + 232 + 126 + 62}{4} = 147.5$$

$$\frac{108 + 50 + 164 + 220}{4} = 135.5 \qquad \frac{232 + 126 + 62 + 180}{4} = 150$$

(c)

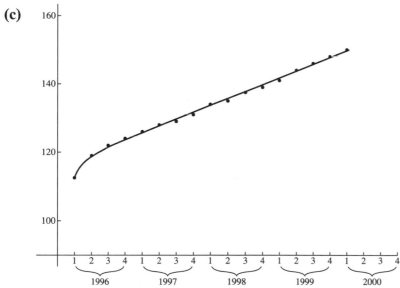

Note that the moving averages are usually plotted between the second and third points used in the average on the horizontal axis.

(d) The trend line shows that there was a steady increase in the gas bills between 1996 and 2000.

Revision exercise 24

1 The waiting time for patients to be seen by a doctor after arriving at the accident and emergency department of a hospital during a weekend period were recorded. The histogram shows the results.

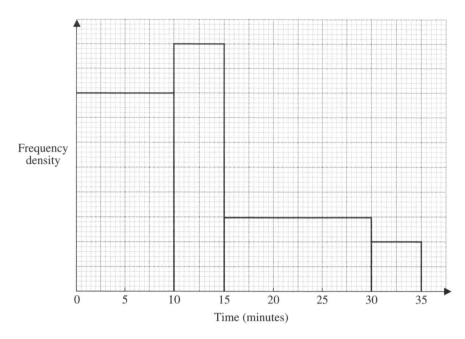

There were exactly 20 patients who were seen by a doctor in a time which was greater than or equal to 10 minutes and less than 15 minutes.

No patient had to wait 35 minutes or longer before being seen by a doctor.

Use the information in the histogram to complete the frequency table.

Waiting time in minutes (t)	Frequency
$0 \leqslant t < 10$	
$10 \leqslant t < 15$	20
$15 \leqslant t < 30$	
$30 \leqslant t < 35$	
$35 \leqslant t$	0

[E]

2 The table below shows Maureen's quarterly oil bills for her central heating over the period from 1998 to 2001.

	1st quarter	2nd quarter	3rd quarter	4th quarter
1998	170	84	50	110
1999	184	90	56	120
2000	202	98	62	132
2001	220	102	70	140

(a) Plot these quarterly bills as a time series.
(b) Work out the four point moving averages for these oil bills.

(c) Plot the moving averages on the same axes as the raw data for the time series.

(d) Comment on the changes in the oil bills over the period from 1998 to 2001.

3 The figures below show the number of cars using a town car park each day during a four-week cycle.

	Mon	Tues	Wed	Thur	Fri	Sat	Sun
Week 1	86	91	212	68	137	207	28
Week 2	84	102	206	72	142	238	40
Week 3	79	81	252	39	153	228	22
Week 4	93	79	216	58	129	232	36

(a) Plot these figures as a time series.

(b) Work out the seven-point moving averages for the figures.

(c) There is a market in the town on two days each week. From the evidence above, suggest, with reasons, which two days of the week the market is held.

4 The table shows the average house prices in Shirecaly over the period from 1980 to 2002.

(a) Plot this data as a time series.

(b) Work out the five-year moving average and plot it on the same axes.

(c) Comment on the data.

£000		£000		£000	
1980	36	1990	70	2000	97
1981	38	91	65	01	101
1982	39	92	64	02	105
1983	42	93	60		
1984	44	94	62		
1985	45	95	67		
1986	48	96	72		
1987	52	97	81		
1988	62	98	86		
1989	70	99	93		

5 The table shows the working life (h) in hours of 120 overhead projector bulbs.

(a) Work out the number of bulbs represented by the square shown as the key.

Number of hours (h)	Frequency
$0 \leqslant h < 20$	10
$20 \leqslant h < 30$	20
$30 \leqslant h < 40$	50
$40 \leqslant h < 60$	30
$60 \leqslant h < 100$	10

(b) Copy and complete the histogram to show the information in the table.

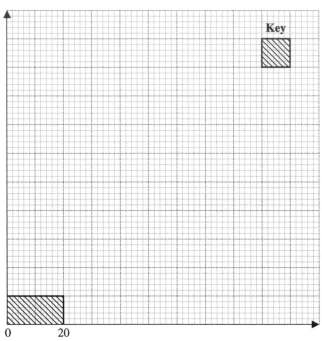

Number of hours (*h*)

6 Jenny works as a sales operator. On top of her salary she receives a bonus payment, according to the number of sales she makes, in March, July and November of each year.

The table below shows her bonus payment (in £1000s) over the period from 1999 to 2002.

	March	July	Nov
1999	4.8	3.6	2.7
2000	5.2	4.1	2.4
2001	5.0	4.3	2.8
2002	5.5	4.6	2.9

(a) Plot this information as a time series.
(b) Work out the three point moving average for the bonus payments.
(c) Plot the three point moving averages on the same axes as the time series.
(d) Explain clearly whether or not there is any evidence to suggest that Jenny's bonus payments are increasing.

7 There are 200 members of Lucea Golf Club.
   The distribution of their ages (*A*) is shown
   in the table opposite.
   Draw a histogram to represent the
   information in the table.

Age (*A*) years	Frequency
$0 \leqslant A < 20$	15
$20 \leqslant A < 30$	35
$30 \leqslant A < 40$	58
$40 \leqslant A < 50$	52
$50 \leqslant A < 60$	20
$60 \leqslant A < 65$	12
$65 \leqslant A < 90$	8

Test yourself   What to review

1 In a survey on October 1st, pupils at Lucea High school were
   asked how long they had taken to go from home to school
   that morning. Each pupil present ticked one and only one of
   the following responses.

   Exactly 96 pupils ticked the '$5 \leqslant t < 15$' box. No pupil ticked
   the '$t \geqslant 70$' box.

Time in minutes *t*	
$0 \leqslant t < 5$	
$5 \leqslant t < 15$	
$15 \leqslant t < 25$	
$25 \leqslant t < 40$	
$40 \leqslant t < 70$	
$t \geqslant 70$	

   The histogram shows the results of the survey.

*If your answer is incorrect,
review in the Higher book:*

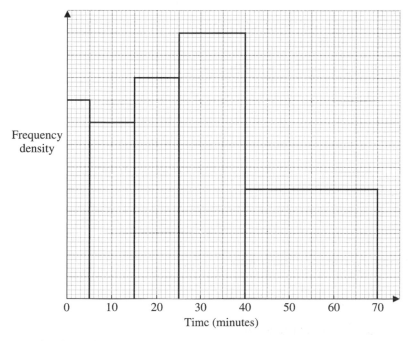

Frequency
density

Time (minutes)

   Calculate the number of pupils who were absent on
   October 1st given that the total number of pupils at the
   school is 726.

Unit 29, Section 29.2
[E] Unit 29, Section 29.2

2 The table below gives Alex's quarterly electricity bills from 1999 to 2002.

	1st quarter	2nd quarter	3rd quarter	4th quarter
1999	270	130	75	160
2000	300	140	80	175
2001	320	152	82	190
2002	332	160	88	212

(a) Plot the data as a time series.

(b) Work out the four-point moving average for the electricity bills.

Unit 15, pages 309–310

Answers to Test yourself

1 60

2 (a)

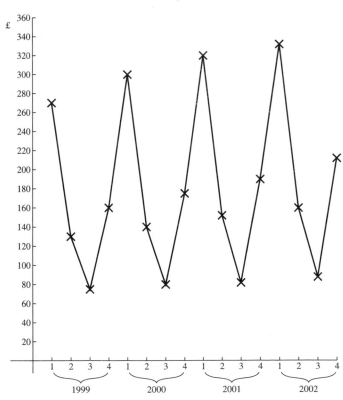

(b) $158.75, 166.25, 168.75, 170.00, 173.75, 178.75, 181.75, 182.25, 186.00, 189.00, 191.00, 192.50, 198.00

25 Probability

Probability is a measure of the likelihood – or chance – of something happening.

Key points to remember

1 $P(\text{event}) = \dfrac{\text{the number of ways the event can occur}}{\text{the total number of possibilities}}$

2 $\text{Relative frequency} = \dfrac{\text{number of times event occurs}}{\text{total number of trials}}$

3 **Probabilities should only be expressed as fractions, decimals or percentages.**

4 **When an event has several separate and mutually exclusive outcomes then the sum of the probabilities of all these outcomes is 1. For example:**
if an event has 3 outcomes, A, B, C then
$$P(A) + P(B) + P(C) = 1$$

Mutually exclusive means that no two outcomes can occur at the same time.

5 **For mutually exclusive events:**
$$P(A \text{ or } B) = P(A) + P(B)$$

6 **Event A and event 'not A' are mutually exclusive and cover all possibilities and so**
$$P(\text{not } A) = 1 - P(A)$$

7 **For independent events:**
$$P(A \text{ and } B) = P(A) \times P(B)$$

Independent means that the outcome of one event does not affect the outcome of the other.

8 **You should know how to set up and use tree diagrams.**

Example 1
There are three candidates for an election. Their names are Abbot, Bailey and Cassell.

Before the election a survey is conducted of the voting intentions of 200 people chosen at random.

The results of the survey are:

Candidate	Number of likely voters
Abbot	120
Bailey	48
Cassell	32

(a)   Use this information to work out an estimate of the probability that a randomly chosen voter will vote for Bailey.

On the day of the election exactly 25 000 votes are cast.
(b)   Estimate, with reasons, the number of votes likely to be cast for Abbot.

On the day of the election, two voters are chosen at random.
(c)   Estimate the probability that:
   (i) they will both vote for Cassell.
   (ii) at least one of them will vote for Cassell.

Answer
(a)   Using **2** the estimated probability, P(Bailey) or P(B), is:

$$P(B) = \frac{\text{number of likely voters for Bailey}}{\text{total number in survey}}$$

$$P(B) = \frac{48}{200} = 0.24$$

(b)   Using **2** P(Abbot) = P(A) = $\frac{120}{200}$ = 0.6

Using **1** the estimate for the likely number of votes cast for Abott is given by:

$$P(A) = \frac{\text{likely number of votes for Abbot}}{\text{total votes cast}}$$

Rearranging:

likely number of votes for Abbot = P(A) × total votes cast
So   likely number of votes for Abbot = 0.6 × 25 000
$$= 15\,000$$

(c)   Using **2**
$$P(\text{Cassell}) = P(C) = \frac{32}{200} = 0.16$$

   (i) Using **7**
$$P(C \text{ and } C) = 0.16 \times 0.16$$
$$= 0.0256$$

(ii) Using **6**

$$P(\text{at least 1 votes for } C) = 1 - P(\text{both do not vote for } C)$$

Using 6 again,

$$\begin{aligned} P(\text{not voting for } C) &= 1 - P(C) \\ &= 1 - 0.16 \\ &= 0.84 \end{aligned}$$

Now using 7

$$\begin{aligned} P(\text{not } C \text{ and not } C) &= 0.84 \times 0.84 \\ &= 0.7056 \end{aligned}$$

So $$\begin{aligned} P(\text{at least 1 votes for } C) &= 1 - 0.7056 \\ &= 0.2944 \end{aligned}$$

Example 2

Kemal has two bags of chocolates.

Bag A contains 15 chocolates.
8 are plain, 4 are milk and 3 are white.

Bag B contains 12 chocolates.
4 are plain, 4 are milk and 4 are white.

Kemal selects a chocolate at random from each bag.
Work out:
(a) the probability that each chocolate selected is plain;
(b) the probability that each chocolate is of the same type;
(c) the probability that at least one chocolate is milk.

Answer

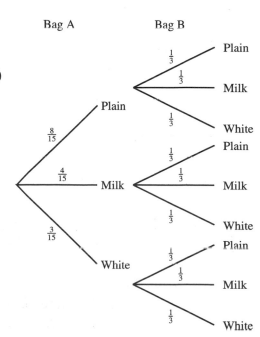

(a) Probability of plain and plain $= \dfrac{8}{15} \times \dfrac{1}{3} = \dfrac{8}{45}$

(b) Probability of both the same $= p(pp) + p(mm) + p(ww)$

$$= \frac{8}{15} \times \frac{1}{3} + \frac{4}{15} \times \frac{1}{3} + \frac{3}{15} \times \frac{1}{3}$$

$$= \frac{8}{45} + \frac{4}{45} + \frac{3}{45} = \frac{15}{45} = \frac{1}{3}$$

(c) Probability (at least one milk)

$$= 1 - (\text{probability both not milk})$$

$$= 1 - \left(\frac{11}{15} \times \frac{2}{3} \right)$$

$$= 1 - \frac{22}{45} = \frac{23}{45}$$

Worked examination question [E]

A bag contains 15 equal sized coloured balls.
6 balls are red, 4 balls are blue and the remaining balls are white.

A ball is selected at random.
(a)   Write down the probability that this ball will be white.

A ball is selected at random and its colour recorded.
This ball is put back in the bag.
A second ball is then selected and its colour recorded.
This ball is also put back in the bag.

(b)   Draw a probability tree diagram.

(c)   Using your tree diagram or otherwise, work out the
      probabilities of
      (i) both recorded colours being blue
      (ii) both recorded colours being the same.

A third ball is then selected at random and its colour recorded.
(d)   Work out the probability of at least two of the recorded
      colours being red.

Answer

(a)   Using **1**
$$P(W) = \tfrac{5}{15} = \tfrac{1}{3}$$

(b)   Using **9** with **8** and **4**, set up the tree diagram as follows:

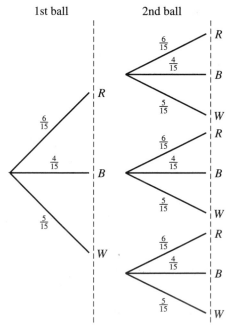

(c)   (i) Using **7** and the tree diagram
$$P(B \text{ and } B) = \tfrac{4}{15} \times \tfrac{4}{15} = \tfrac{16}{225}$$

(ii) Using **5** and **7** again

$$P(\text{both same}) = P(RR) + P(BB) + P(WW)$$
$$= \frac{6}{15} \times \frac{6}{15} + \frac{4}{15} \times \frac{4}{15} + \frac{5}{15} \times \frac{5}{15}$$
$$= \frac{36}{225} + \frac{16}{225} + \frac{25}{225}$$
$$= \frac{77}{225}$$

(d) Extend the appropriate parts of the tree diagram to cover all cases with at least two red:

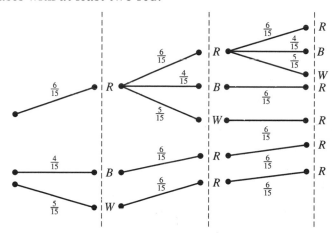

Using **7** probability of at least two red is:

$$\left(\frac{6}{15} \times \frac{6}{15} \times \frac{6}{15}\right) + \left(\frac{6}{15} \times \frac{6}{15} \times \frac{4}{15}\right) + \left(\frac{6}{15} \times \frac{6}{15} \times \frac{5}{15}\right) + \left(\frac{6}{15} \times \frac{4}{15} \times \frac{6}{15}\right) + \left(\frac{6}{15} \times \frac{5}{15} \times \frac{6}{15}\right)$$
$$+ \left(\frac{4}{15} \times \frac{6}{15} \times \frac{6}{15}\right) + \left(\frac{5}{15} \times \frac{6}{15} \times \frac{6}{15}\right)$$

Note, the top row is:

$$\left(\frac{6}{15} \times \frac{5}{14}\right) \times \left(\frac{4}{13} + \frac{4}{13} + \frac{5}{13}\right) = \frac{6}{15} \times \frac{5}{14} \times 1 = \frac{30}{210}$$

So $$P(\text{at least 2 red}) = \frac{216 + 144 + 180 + 144 + 180 + 144 + 180}{15^3}$$

$$= \frac{1188}{3375}$$

$$P(\text{at least 2 red}) = \frac{44}{125}$$

Example 3

Vandana is due to take her driving test.
The probability that she will pass the test at the first attempt is p.
Should she fail at the first attempt then the probability that she will pass at the second or any subsequent attempt is q.

Prove that the probability of Vandana passing the driving test in **at most two** attempts is

$$p + q - pq.$$

Answer

Using a tree diagram:

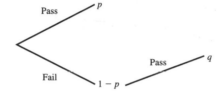

1st attempt

2nd attempt

q

Pass

p

Pass

Fail

$1 - q$

Pass

q

Fail

$1 - p$

Fail

$1 - q$

To pass in two attempts at most, we need to consider the branches:

1st attempt   2nd attempt

p

Pass

Pass

q

Fail

$1 - p$

i.e. she must either

pass (1st attempt) or fail (1st) and pass (2nd)

$= p + (1 - p)q$

$= p + q - pq.$

Hence proven.

Revision exercise 25

1 Peter and Asif are both taking their driving test for a motorcycle for the first time.

The table below gives the probabilities that they will pass the test at the first attempt or, if they fail the first time, the probability that they will pass at the next attempt.

	Probability of passing at first attempt	Probability of passing at next attempt if they fail the first attempt
Peter	0.5	0.8
Asif	0.8	0.9

On a particular day 2000 people will take the test for the first time.

For each person the probability that they will pass the test at the first attempt is the same as the probability that Asif will pass the test at the first attempt.

(a) Work out an estimate for how many of these 2000 people are likely to pass the test at the first attempt.

(b) Calculate the probability that both Peter and Asif will pass the test at the first attempt.

(c) Calculate the probability that Peter will pass the test at the first attempt and Asif will fail the test at the first attempt.

(d) Calculate the probability that Asif will pass the test within the first two attempts. [E adapted]

2 There are two sets of traffic lights on Paul's route to school.

The probability that the first set of lights will be green is $\frac{3}{5}$.

If he finds the first set of lights green, the probability that the second set of lights will be green, when he gets to them, is $\frac{2}{7}$.

If he finds the first set of lights are not green, the probability that the second set of lights will be green, when he gets to them, is $\frac{4}{7}$.

(a) Draw a tree diagram for this situation.

(b) Calculate the probability that Paul will find the first set of lights is not green and the second set of lights is green.

(c) Calculate the probability that Paul will find the second set of lights is green.

3 A bag contains 12 equal sized coloured balls. 7 of the balls are red, 2 are blue and 3 are green.

A ball is selected, at random, from the bag, and then replaced. Another ball is then selected.
Work out the probability of both balls being the same colour.

4 Heather has five red scarves, four white scarves and three blue scarves.
She chooses a scarf at random to wear at work.

Bavines has six red scarves and four white scarves.
She also chooses a scarf at random to wear at work.

Calculate the probability that Heather and Bavines will wear the same colour scarf to work tomorrow. [E}

5 James is due to take a music examination.
The probability that he will pass at the first attempt is 0.6.
If he fails at the first attempt, the probability of passing at the second or any subsequent attempt is 0.8.

Work out the probability that he will pass in 3 attempts at most. [E]

6 A fair coin is tossed 5 times.
Work out the probability that it will land Heads on all 5
occasions.

Test yourself	**What to review**

1 A bag contains some red, some white and some blue counters.
A counter is picked at random.
The probability that it will be red is 0.2.
The probability that it will be white is 0.3.

If your answer is incorrect,
review in the Higher book:

   (a) What is the probability that a counter picked at random
   will be either red or white?

   Unit 9, Example 3
   Unit 9, Example 3

   (b) What is the probability that a counter picked at random
   will be either red or blue?

   Unit 9, Example 4
   Unit 9, Example 4

A counter will be picked at random. Its colour will be
recorded. The counter will be put back in the bag.

A second counter will be picked at random.
Its colour will be recorded.

   (c) By drawing a tree diagram, or otherwise, calculate the
   probability that the first counter will be red and the second
   counter will be white.

   Unit 9, Sections 9.5 and 9.6
   Unit 9, Sections 9.5 and 9.6

   (d) Calculate the probability that both counters will be white.

   Unit 9, Sections 9.5 and 9.6
   Unit 9, Sections 9.5 and 9.6

2 Fatima is due to take her motorcycle driving test.

The probability that she will pass at the first attempt is 0.7.

If she fails at the first attempt, then the probability that she
will pass at the second or any subsequent attempt is 0.9.

   (a) Prove that the probability of Fatima passing the driving
   test in **at most** two attempts is greater than 95%.

   Unit 9, Section 9.6
   Unit 9, Section 9.6

   (b) Prove that the probability of Fatima passing the driving
   test in **at most** three attempts is greater than 99%.

Answers to Test yourself

1 (a) 0.5   **(b)** 0.7   **(c)** 0.06 **(d)** 0.09   **2   (a)** probability (at most > 1) = 0.97   **(b)** probability (at most 3) = 0.997

If your answer is incorrect, review in this book:

You may not use a calculator in this section.

1 A shop has a sale and reduces all its prices by 20%
   (a) Work out the sale price of a coat which had a price of £70
      before the sale.   (2 marks)   *Unit 2, Key point* **2**

   The price of a dress in the sale is £32.
   (b) Work out the price of this dress before the sale.

                                                (2 marks)   *Unit 2, Example 3*

2 (a) Solve the equation

   $$5(x - 3) = 7 + 2x$$ (3 marks)   *Unit 5, Example 1*

   (b) Solve the equation

   $$y^2 + 1 = 28$$ (2 marks)   *Unit 6, Key points* **2** , **3**
                                                                and **4**

3

The diagram represents a biased spinner. Jane spun the
Spinner 200 times and recorded the section upon which it
stopped each time. Her results were:

Section	A	B	C	D	E
Frequency	43	62	58	26	11

Tom spun the spinner 300 times and also recorded the section
upon which it stopped each time. His results were:

Section	A	B	C	D	E
Frequency	65	88	86	41	20

The spinner is to be spun once more. Work out, with reasons,
the best estimate of the probability that it will stop on the
section marked **B**. Give your answer in its lowest terms.
                                                (4 marks)

4 Solve the simultaneous equations
      $$4x - y = 13$$
      $$3x + 2y = 7$$ (3 marks)   *Unit 5, Key point* **3**

If your answer is incorrect, review in this book:

5 A, B, C and D lie on the circumference of a circle. TA is a tangent to the circle at A. $AB = AD$.

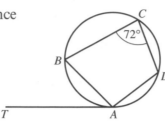

Work out, giving your reasons, the angle TAB.   (3 marks)   *Unit 20, Key points* ◼5–◼8

6

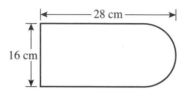

The diagram represents a metal plate made from a rectangle with a semi-circular end.
Work out the area of the plate, giving your answer in cm^2 and leaving it in terms of π.   (5 marks)   *Unit 3, Key point* ◼9

7 **(a)** Simplify $n^3 \times n^5$.   (1 mark)   *Unit 1, Key point* ◼1

   (b) Expand and simplify $4(3x + 5) - 2(x - 3)$.   (2 marks)

   (c) Factorize $5a - 15$.   (1 mark)   *Unit 1, Key point* ◼10

   (d) Factorize completely:
   $$2x^3 y + 6xy^3$$
   (2 marks)   *Unit 1, Key point* ◼10

   (e) Solve the equation:
   $$\frac{7 + 2x}{x} = -3$$
   (3 marks)   *Unit 5, Key point* ◼2

   (f) (i) Factorize $x^2 - 3x - 28$.
   (ii) Hence or otherwise, solve the equation:
   $x^2 - 3x - 28 = 0$.   (4 marks)   *Unit 1, Key point* ◼11

8 Lizzie has the following information about the oil bills for her home over the period from 2001 to 2002.

Year	1st quarter	2nd quarter	3rd quarter	4th quarter
2001	222	120	58	172
2002	234	128	64	182

   (a) Plot these quarterly bills as a time series.   (1 mark)   *Unit 24, Key point* ◼7

   (b) Work out the four-point moving averages.   (2 marks)   *Unit 24, Key point* ◼6

   (c) On the same axes as the time series, plot the moving averages and draw the trend line.   (2 marks)   *Unit 24, Key point* ◼7

   (d) Make three comments about the variations in Lizzie's oil bills from 2001 to 2002.   (3 marks)   *Unit 24, Example 2*

If your answer is incorrect, review in this book:

9 Prove that the difference between the squares of two successive odd numbers is a multiple of 8. (4 marks)

Unit 1, Key point **12**

10 (a) Work out the exact value of $8.78^2 - 1.22^2$. (2 marks)

Unit 1, Key point **12**

(b) Express each of the following decimals as fractions in the form $\dfrac{n}{m}$, where n and m are integers:

(i) $0.2\dot{3}\dot{7}$

(ii) $0.5\dot{1}\dot{4}$ (4 marks)

Unit 3, Key point **3** *Worked examination question 1*

11 The incomplete table and histogram show some information about the heights of a sample of boys.

Unit 24, Key points **4**, **5**

Height (h) in cm	Frequency
$140 \leqslant h < 145$	10
$145 \leqslant h < 148$	15
$148 \leqslant h < 150$	20
$150 \leqslant h < 154$	
$154 \leqslant h < 157$	9

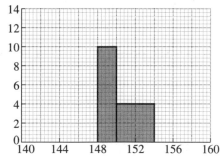

(a) Use the information in the histogram to complete the table. (1 mark)

(b) Use the information in the table to complete the histogram. (2 marks)

12 (a) Sketch the graph of
$$x^2 + y^2 = 25.$$
(2 marks)

Unit 10, Key point **7**

(b) Calculate the area bounded by the graph of $x^2 + y^2 = 25$, the positive x axis and the positive y axis, leaving your answer in terms of π. (2 marks)

Unit 10, Example 3

13 The radius of a sphere is r cm. The volume of the sphere, in cm^3, is numerically equal to the diameter, in cm.

Show that $r = \sqrt{\dfrac{3}{2\pi}}$ (4 marks)

Unit 19, Key point **4**

If your answer is incorrect, review in this book:

14 Express as a single algebraic fraction:

$$\frac{2}{x-1} - \frac{1}{x+3}$$ (3 marks)

Unit 1, Key point **8**, *Worked examination question 3*

15 Peter is due to take his driving test. The probability that he will pass at the first attempt is 0.7. If he fails at the first attempt, the probability that he will pass on the second or any subsequent attempt is 0.8.
Work out the probability that he will pass the driving test in two attempts at most. (3 marks)

Unit 25, Key points **5**, **6**, **7** *Example 3*

16 The equation of a graph is $y = ax + b$, where a and b are fixed numbers and x and y are variables.
The equation of a second graph is $y = mx + c$, where m and c are fixed numbers.

(a) Show that the x coordinate of the point of intersection of the two graphs is given by:

$$x = \frac{c-b}{a-m}$$ (3 marks)

Unit 5, Key points **1**, **2**

(b) Explain clearly what happens in the case where $a = m$ and $c = b$. (2 marks)

Unit 10, Key points **1**, **2**

17 A is the point $(2, 5)$, B is the point $(-2, 2)$ and O is the point $(0, 0)$.

Unit 19, Worked examination question 1

(a) (i) Write $\overrightarrow{AB}$ as a column vector.

(ii) Find the length of the vector $\overrightarrow{AB}$.

D is the point such that $\overrightarrow{BD}$ is parallel to $\begin{pmatrix} 0 \\ 1 \end{pmatrix}$ and the length of $\overrightarrow{AD}$ = length of $\overrightarrow{AB}$.

(b) Find $\overrightarrow{OD}$ as a column vector. (2 marks)

C is the point such that ABCD is a rhombus, with AC as a diagonal.

(c) Find the coordinates of C. (2 marks)

18 (a) Factorize $4x^2 - y^2$. (1 mark)

Unit 1, Key point **12**

(b) Given that $4x^2 - y^2 = 35$ and $2x + y = 7$, find the values of x and y. (4 marks)

Unit 5, Key point **3** *and Unit 10, Worked example 5*

19 (a) Simplify $(x^n)^m$. (1 mark)

Unit 1, Key point **2**

(b) Work out the exact value of $125^{\frac{2}{3}}$ (2 marks)

(c) Put in order, smallest first:

$$2^{29}, \quad 4^{14}, \quad 8^{12}, \quad 16^4, \quad 32^7$$ (2 marks)

Unit 1, Key points **2**, **7**

If your answer is incorrect, review in this book:

20 The equation of a curve is
$$y = x^2 - 6x + 11.$$

   (a) Express the equation in the form
$$y = (x + n)^2 + m.$$
   (3 marks)   *Unit 6, Key point* **3**

   (b) Hence, or otherwise, find the coordinates of the point on the curve for which y has a minimum value.   (2 marks)   *Unit 9, Key point* **2**

You may use a calculator in the section below.

1

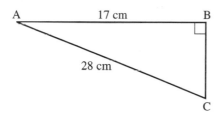

ABC is a triangle with AB = 17 cm, AC = 28 cm and angle ABC = 90°. Work out the value of the perimeter of ABC, giving your answer in centimetres and correct to two decimal places.   (4 marks)   *Unit 12, Key point* **1**

2 A solution of the equation $x^3 - 4x = 30$ lies in the range $3 < x < 4$. Use a method of trial and improvement to work out the solution of $x^3 - 4x = 30$ correct to one decimal place.   (4 marks)   *Unit 5, Key point* **5** *and Worked examination question 2(d)*

3 A survey was carried out to find how minutes late the Express was in June 2002. The results are shown below.   *Unit 22, Worked examination question*

Time (t) minutes late	Number of days
$0 < t < 4$	6
$4 < t < 8$	8
$8 < t < 12$	12
$12 < t < 16$	3
$16 < t < 20$	1

   (a) Draw the frequency polygon for this distribution.   (2 marks)

   (b) Work out an estimate of the mean number of minutes the Express was late.   (4 marks)

   A day in June was picked at random.

   (c) Work out the probability that the Express was 10 or more minutes late on that day.   (2 marks)

If your answer is incorrect, review in this book:

4 P is the point with coordinates $(-2, 7)$.
Q is the point with coordinates $(4, 4)$.

Unit 10, Key point **1**

(a) Work out the coordinates of the midpoint of the line segment PQ. (2 marks)

(b) Work out the equation of the line passing through P and Q. (2 marks)

5 There are approximately 37 500 families living in Lucea.

Unit 2, Key point **8**

(a) Write the number 37 500 in standard form. (1 mark)

The average number of people living in each family in Lucea is 4.4.

(b) Work out an estimate for the number of people living in Lucea. Give your answer in standard form. (2 marks)

6 A solid metal cylinder has a circular base of diameter 12 cm. The height of the cylinder is 15 cm.

Unit 18, Key point **2**

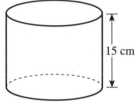

15 cm

(a) Work out the volume of the cylinder in cm^3, giving your answer correct to two decimal places. (2 marks)

The cylinder is melted down and re-case as a solid cube of side x cm.

(b) Work out the value of x. (2 marks)

7 Use your calculator to work out the value of

$$\sqrt{\frac{18.73^2 + 21.24}{4.82 \times 13.07}}$$

Give your answer correct to two decimal places. (3 marks)

8 A bag contains 15 equal-sized coloured balls: 8 white, 4 red, 3 green.

A ball is selected at random from the bag and its colour is recorded. The ball is then put back in the bag. A second ball is selected at random from the bag and the colour recorded.

(a) Draw a probability tree diagram for this situation. Label the branches of the diagram with the appropriate probabilities. (2 marks)

Unit 25, Key point **8** *and Example 2*

(b) Using your tree diagram or otherwise, work out the probabilities that:
  (i) both balls selected will be red
  (ii) both balls selected will be of the same colour.
  (iii) at least one ball will be red. (7 marks)

Unit 25, Key point **7**

If your answer is incorrect, review in this book:

9 Vandana puts £2400 into a building society account. She leaves the money in the account for five years. She does not put any more money into this account. The building society pays compound interest at a rate of 3.5% during those five years. How much will Vandana have in that account at the end of the five years? (3 marks)

Unit 2, Key point **3**

10 Draw the graph of $y = x^3 - 4$. (3 marks)

Unit 8, Key point **4**

11 The speeds in miles per hour of 120 vehicles on a main road are recorded below.

Unit 23, Example 1

Speed (s) mph	Frequency
$0 < s < 10$	3
$10 < s < 20$	18
$20 < s < 30$	46
$30 < s < 40$	32
$40 < s < 50$	16
$50 < s < 60$	4
$60 < s < 70$	3

(a) Copy and complete the cumulative frequency table. (1 mark)

Speed (s) mph	10	20	30	40	50	60	70
Cumulative frequency	3	21					120

(b) Draw the cumulative frequency curve. (2 marks)

The speed limit on the road is 45 mph.

(c) Use your cumulative frequency curve to work out an estimate of the number of vehicles exceeding the speed limit. (2 marks)

(d) Draw a box plot for this distribution. (4 marks)

12 In the triangle, AC = 7 cm and BC = 12 cm. Work out the angle marked $x°$. Give your answer, in degrees, correct to one decimal place. (3 marks)

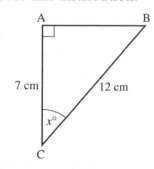

Diagram NOT accurately drawn.

Unit 12, Key point **3**

If your answer is incorrect, review in this book:

13 Given that $(2x + 5)(x - 1) = 4$:

   (a) Show that $2x^2 + 3x - 9 = 0$.   (2 marks)

   (b) Solve the equation $2x^2 + 3x - 9 = 0$.   (3 marks)   *Unit 6, Key point* **2**

14 The diagram represents the path taken by a ship. The ship leaves a harbour, H, and travels 45 km to a marker buoy, B. At B the ship turns on a bearing of 048° and travels a further 32 km to a lighthouse, L.
At L the ship turns again and travels in a straight line back to H.
Calculate the total distance travelled by the ship.

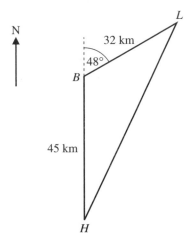

                                       (4 marks)   *Unit 15, Key point* **3**

15 The table shows the number of students in each of the five Year 11 mathematics classes at Jordan Hill County High School.

Mathematics class	Number of students
A1	36
A2	30
A3	25
A4	19
A5	10

   As part of his statistics project, Geoff needs to take a random selected stratified sample according to each class. The size of the sample needs to be 70. How many students from Class A1 should be in the sample?   (3 marks)

Unit 21, Key point **2**, *Example 1*

16 To the nearest whole number, $n = 20$ and $m = 10$.

   (a) Work out the upper bound of $\dfrac{n}{m}$ (3 marks)   *Unit 4, Key points* **1**, **2**

   (b) Work out the lower bound of $\dfrac{n+m}{n}$ (2 marks)

Unit 4, Worked examination question 2

If your answer is incorrect, review in this book:

17 s is inversely proportional to t^2.
When $t = 2$, $s = 25$.
    (i) Find the value of s when $t = 5$.
    (ii) Find the values of t when $s = 10$. Leave your answer
        in surd form   (6 marks)   *Unit 8, Key point* **6**

18 VABC is a tetrahedron.
The vertex V is vertically above B.
The horizontal base is the triangle ABC.
AB = 7 cm, BC = 15 cm and VC = 17 cm.
The angles ABC, VBA and VBC are all right angles.   *Unit 12, Example 1*

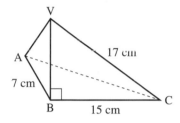

(a) Work out the lengths of
    (i) AC   **(iii)** VB.   (3 marks)

(b) Work out the angle AVB.   (3 marks)

(c) Work out the volume of VABC.   (2 marks)

19 The diagram represents a child's toy.
The toy is made from a cone on a
hemispherical base. The height of the
cone is 15 m. The radius of the base of
the cone and the radius of the hemisphere
are both 12 cm.
Calculate the volume of the toy. Give your
answer in cubic centimetres and correct
to two decimal places.   *Unit 18, Key points* **3**, **4**

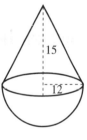

20

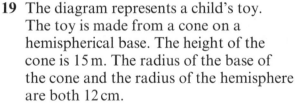

ABC is a triangle with the angle BAC = 90°.
In centimetres, the lengths of the sides are:
AB = x, AC = $x + 7$, BC = $x + 9$.

(a) Prove that $x - 4x - 32 = 0$.   (4 marks)   *Unit 12, Key point* **1**

(b) Work out the shortest distance from A to the side BC.   *Unit 12, Key point* **1** *and*
        (3 marks)   *Worked examination
question (c)*

Answers

Revision exercise 1

1 (a) 8   (b) $\frac{1}{3}$

2 (a) 1   (b) $\frac{1}{8}$

3 (a) 5   (b) $\frac{1}{2}$ (c) $4\frac{1}{2}$

4 (a) $5x(2x-1)$ (b) $3\frac{1}{2}$

5 (a) $3x^2y^2(2-x^2)$ (b) $4xy(3y^2-2x^3)$

6 $(x+y)(a-b)$

7 (a) a^9 (b) x^6 (c) $12x^5$ (d) x^4
   (e) $3x^3$ (f) $\pm\frac{1}{4}$ (g) 32   (h) 1024   (i) 9

8 (a) $\dfrac{2x+y}{xy}$ (b) $\dfrac{13}{6x}$ (c) $\dfrac{2x}{3}$ (d) $\dfrac{-9-3x}{(x+2)(x-1)}$

9 (a) $x(x+4)$ (b) $2xy(x-3y)$ (c) $(x+1)(x+2)$
   (d) $(x-1)(x-4)$ (e) $(x-1)(x+8)$ (f) $(x+4)(x+8)$
   (g) $(2x+1)(x+2)$ (h) $(3x+1)(5x-3)$ (i) $(2x-3)(4x-1)$
   (j) $(2x^2-1)(x^2+4)$ (k) $(x+3)^2$ (l) $(x-4)^2$

10 (a) $(x+6)^2-36$ (b) $25-(x-5)^2$

11 $p=-3\frac{1}{2}$ $q=1$

12 (a) $y\min=3$ (b) $x=-4$

Revision exercise 2

1 £201.60

2 £4419.69

3 3520, 1760, 1320

4 3.818×10^3

5 (a) 1.8×10^9 (b) £720   (c) 2.2×10^6

6 (a) 3×10^{-8} (b) 3×10^{-10}

7 (a) 1.47×10^8 (b) 2.1×10^3 (c) 7×10^4

8 (a) 20%   (b) £6

9 £92

10 (a) 3.62×10^8 (b) 5.12×10^8 (c) 71%

11 $\frac{9}{16}$

12 $\frac{289}{49}$ or $5\frac{44}{49}$

13 $\frac{48}{115}$

Revision exercise 3

1 (a) $\frac{\sqrt{5}}{5}$ (b) $\frac{\sqrt{7}}{14}$

2 $\frac{9\pi}{2}\,\text{cm}^2$ or $4.5\pi\,\text{cm}^2$

3 (a) $\frac{427}{999}$ (b) $\frac{323}{990}$

4 $x=\pm5\sqrt{2}$

5 (a) (i) 91   (ii) $\frac{91}{99}$ (b) $\frac{99}{101}$ and many more.

6 $\dfrac{1}{\sqrt{7}}+\dfrac{1}{\sqrt{3}}=\dfrac{\sqrt{7}}{7}+\dfrac{\sqrt{3}}{3}=\dfrac{3\sqrt{7}+7\sqrt{3}}{7\times3}=\dfrac{3\sqrt{7}+7\sqrt{3}}{21}$

Revision exercise 4

1 (a) 12.5, 12.7
   (b) Yes as this lies within the upper and lower bound

2 (a) (i) 31.894 762 5   (ii) 29.442 262 5
   (b) 30

3 (a) $176.527\,331\,2 <$ length $< 178.317\,152\,1$ (b) 2

4 (a) 2.86   (b) $66.517\,315\,07\,\text{cm}^2$ $66.427\,956\,79\,\text{cm}^2$

5 75.3 cm

6 (a) $380\,\text{cm}^2$ (b) $460\,\text{cm}^2$

7 (a) (i) 2.2365   (ii) 2.2355   (b) (i) 3.651 (ii) 3.649
   (c) 3.159 879 25   (d) 1.582 242 66

8 (a) 3   (b) $\frac{17}{7}$ or $2\frac{3}{7}$

Revision exercise 5

1 (a) $x=6$ (b) $x=-3$ (c) $x=7\frac{1}{5}$ (d) $x=\frac{5}{7}$
   (e) $x=2$ (f) $x=\frac{9}{11}$ (g) $x=\frac{15}{13}$ or $1\frac{2}{3}$ (h) $x=-6$

2 (a) $p=2$, $q=-1$ (b) $x=5$, $y=-2$
   (c) $p=3$, $q=-3$ (d) $x=4$, $y=-2$

3 (a) (b) $x=0$, or $x=3$

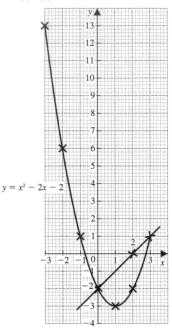

$y=x^2-2x-2$

4 (a) (c)

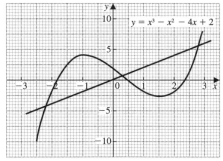

(b) $m=2$, $c=0$
(d) $x=2.8$, 0.3, -2.2

5 (a)

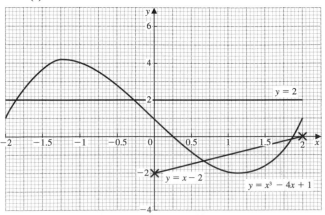

$y=2$

$y=x-2$ $y=x^3-4x+1$

(b) 0.25, 1.75
(c) (i) $y=2$, $x=-0.25$ or -1.75
   (ii) $y=x-2$, $x=0.65$ or 1.85

6

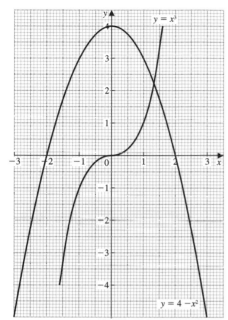

$x = 1.3$

7   4.3

8   2.4

Revision exercise 6

1 (a) $\pm\sqrt{5}$ (b) 0, 7   (c) $-3, -4$
   (d) $6, -3$ (e) $-6, -4$ (f) $8, -2$
   (g) $-\frac{1}{2}, 3$ (h) $-\frac{2}{5}, 5$ (i) $\frac{1}{2}, -\frac{5}{3}$

2 (a) (i) $\frac{1}{2}(7+\sqrt{61}), \frac{1}{2}(7-\sqrt{61})$ (ii) 7.41, -0.41
   (b) (i) $\frac{1}{3}(2+\sqrt{10}), \frac{1}{3}(2-\sqrt{10})$ (ii) 1.72, -0.39
   (c) (i) $\frac{1}{2}(3+\sqrt{13}), \frac{1}{2}(3-\sqrt{13})$ (ii) 3.30, -0.30
   (d) (i) $-\frac{1}{4}(3-\sqrt{41}), -\frac{1}{4}(3+\sqrt{41})$ (ii) 0.85, -2.35
   (e) (i) $\frac{1}{6}(7+\sqrt{37}), \frac{1}{6}(7-\sqrt{37})$ (ii) 2.18, 0.15

3 (a)

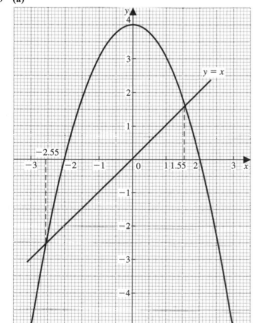

(b) 1.55, -2.55

4 (a) $\dfrac{20}{x} + \dfrac{20}{x+2} = 4$ (c) $6+\sqrt{26}, 6-\sqrt{26}$

   (d) $x = 0.9$ gives a negative speed on homeward journey

5 (a) $\dfrac{12}{x} + \dfrac{12}{x-2}$ (b) (i) $\dfrac{12}{x} + \dfrac{12}{x-2} = \dfrac{7}{2}$

   (c) $x = 8$

Revision exercise 7

1 (a) $x \geqslant 2$ (b) $x \leqslant \frac{1}{3}$ (c) $x \leqslant 4\frac{1}{2}$ (d) $x \leqslant \frac{6}{7}$
   (e) $x \geqslant -6$ (f) $x \leqslant 3$ (g) $x \leqslant \frac{2}{3}$ (h) $x < \frac{5}{3}$

2

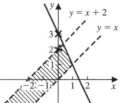

3

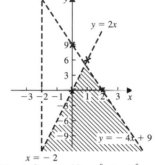

4 (a) $-6 < x < 6$ (b) $-9 > x > 9$ (c) $-\frac{8}{3} < x < \frac{8}{3}$
   (d) $-8 \geqslant x \geqslant 6$ (e) $8 > x > -2$ (f) $-\frac{5}{3} < x < \frac{7}{3}$

5 (a) $x \leqslant 1\frac{3}{4}$ (b)

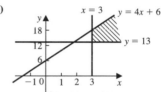

Revision exercise 8

1 (a) $c = 1.4a$
   (b) (i) 70p   (ii) 98p   (iii) £1.89   (iv) £3.08
   (c) 125 ml
2 (a) $d = kt^2$ (b) $k = 5$ (c) 80 m   (d) 10 s
3 (a) $f = \dfrac{k}{w}$ (b) $k = 3200$ (c) (i) 640   (ii) 16 000
   (d) 0.64
4 3.83 litres
5 (a) $a = kb^3$ (b) $k = 2$ (c) 432   (d) 7
6 (a) 500   (b) ± 6
7 180 feet
8 (a) $t = \dfrac{k}{V}$ (b) 40 000

Revision exercise 9

1 (a) -3 (b) 2
   (c) 17   (d) 122
2 (a)   (b)

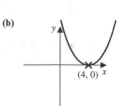

3 (a) (i) Same graph translated -1 vertically along y-axis.
    (ii) Same graph translated -1 horizontally along x-axis.

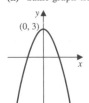

(b)

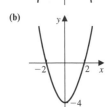

4 (a)

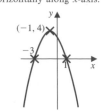

(b) $-\frac{1}{2}$ (c) 2, -4

5

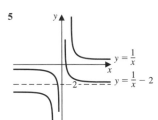

6

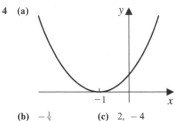

$y = (x+1)^2 + 3$

7 (a) (b)

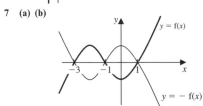

(c) A reflection in the x-axis

8

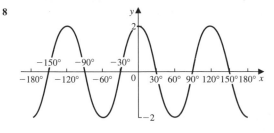

Revision exercise 10

1 (a) $-\frac{3}{2}$ (b) $c = 6$ (c) $y = -\frac{3x}{2} + 7$ (d) $y = \frac{2}{3}x + 9$

2 (a)

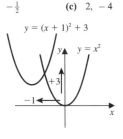

gradient $= \frac{-1}{2}$

(0, 7)

(b) $y = 2x + 9$

3 (a) $0.8\,\text{m}\,\text{s}^{-2}$ (b) $144\,\text{m}$ (c) $\frac{4}{7}\,\text{m}\,\text{s}^{-2}$

4 (a)

(b) $1200\,\text{m}$

5 39.3 square units   **6** 20π square units

7 $x = 1 \pm \sqrt{17}$ $y = 1 \pm \sqrt{17}$

8 $x = 3, y = -1$

9 $x = 2, y = 3$ $x = -1, y = 0$

10 $x^2 + y^2 = 25$ is a circle with centre $(0, 0)$ and radius 5; $y = ax - 3$ crosses the y-axis at $(0, -3)$ – a point which is inside the circle. So any line through this point must cut the circle in two places.

Revision exercise 11

1 $p = 3, q = 4, y = 3(4)^x$

2 $p = 2^{\frac{1}{3}}, q = 2^{\frac{2}{3}}, y = 2^{\frac{1}{3}}(2^{\frac{1}{3}})^x = 2^{\frac{x+2}{3}}$

3 (a)

(b) $p = 5000, q = 0.6$

4 (a)

(b) $a = 2.5, b = 0.5$

5 (a)

(b) $a = 6.4, b = 39$

6 (a)

(b) $a = 2.5, b = 1.2$

7 (a) (i) t^2 values: 0.3136, 0.5041, 0.9409, 1.1236, 1.2544, 1.5625

     (ii) The values all lie on a straight line passing through the origin.

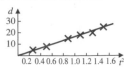

(b) 16

Revision exercise 12

1 (a) 40.97 cm   (b) 50.91 cm²   (c) 19.5°
2 (a) 300 km   (b) 337°   (c) 46.2 km
3 (a) 16.16 cm   (b) 16.91 cm   (c) 17.2°
4 13.4 m
5 (a) 8 cm   (b) 28.3 cm   (c) 28.1°   (d) 15.8°
6 (a) 16.97 cm   (b) 8.485 cm   (c) 70.2°
7 (a) 77.3°   (b) 9 cm   (c) 15 cm   (d) 73.3°
8 24.57 cm
9 Examples include:
   (a) 3, 4, 5   (b) 3, √3, √6   (c) √2, 1, 1   (d) 2, 1, √3

Revision exercise 13

1 16 m
2 (a) 5.25 cm   (b) ECD, FCE
3 P'(0, −1), Q'(−1, −1), R'(−1, −3)
4 (a) CÂB = YX̂B;   B̂ common. So corresponding angles are equal.
   (b) 6⁶⁄₇   (c) ⁴⁹⁄₁₆
5 S, S″ are congruent. Overall scale factor is −1.
6 4⁸⁄₁₃ cm

Revision exercise 14

1

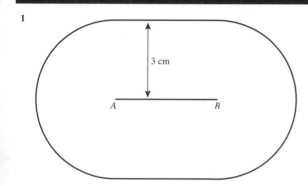

2

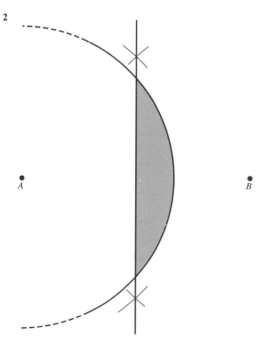

3

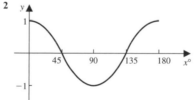

4 Both triangles share side PO; sides OB and OA are both equal (radii of circle centre O); sides BP and AP are equal (tangents from a point) ⇒ SSS
5 Side AB is common to both triangles; angle BÂC = angle AB̂D; angle AD̂B = angle AĈB ⇒ SAA

Revision exercise 15

1 (a) x = 8.08 cm, area = 32.1 cm²   (b) x = 12.4 cm, area = 25.4 cm²
2 283°   3 (b) 5
4 (a) 43.3 km   (b) 7.2 km/h and 10.87 km/h
5 33.6 m   6 36.9°
7 (a) 23.35 m   (b) 62.7°
8 (a) 52.34° and 127.66°   (b) 9.52 cm and 18.04 cm
9 (a) 203.56 km   (b) 047°   (c) 30.71 km
10 17.3°

Revision exercise 16

1 15°, 75°
2

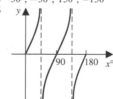

3 71.56° only   4 60°, 300°, −60°, −300°
5 30°, −30°, 150°, −150°
6

7 (a) max = 5 at x = 90°   (b) min = −5 at x = 270°
8 53.13° and −53.13°

Revision exercise 17

1 (a) Translation, 6 units to the right
   (b) Translation, 6 units to the left
2 (a) (i)   (ii)

   (b) Rotation about the point of intersection of the two lines through an angle twice the size of the angle between the two lines.

3 **(a)** Rotation 180° about $\left(-\frac{1}{2}, \frac{1}{2}\right)$
  (b) Rotation 180° about $\left(-\frac{1}{2}, \frac{1}{2}\right)$
4 Rotation about $(0, 0)$ through 90° anticlockwise.
5 **(a)** $A''(6, 6)$ $B''(12, 6)$ $C''(6, 18)$
  (b) Enlargement, scale factor 6, centre $(0, 0)$.
6 **(a)** Enlargement centre X, scale factor k^2.
  (b) Enlargement centre X, scale factor $\dfrac{1}{k^2}$.

Revision exercise 18

1 $15\,\text{cm}^2$ **2** **(a)** $1230\,\text{m}$ **(b)** $31\,400$
3 $1005.3\,\text{cm}^3$ **4** **(a)** $20\,\text{cm}$ **(b)** $21.93\,\text{cm}$
5 **(a)** $5.20\,\text{cm}$ **(b)** $589.5\,\text{cm}^3$ **6** $869.3\,\text{cm}^3$
7 $27.95\,\text{cm}$ **8** **(a)** $301.6\,\text{cm}^3$ **(b)** $271\,\text{g}$
9 **(a)** $200 + \frac{400\pi}{9}\,\text{m}$ **(b)** $\frac{20\,000}{9}\pi\,\text{m}^2$
10 **(a)** $169.65\,\text{cm}^3$ **(b)** $2.95\,\text{cm}$ **(c)** 6.7%

Revision exercise 19

1 **(a)**
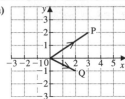

(b) $\begin{pmatrix} 5 \\ 1 \end{pmatrix}$
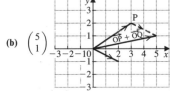
(c) $\begin{pmatrix} 1 \\ 3 \end{pmatrix}$

2 $a + 4b = \begin{pmatrix} 10 \\ 12 \end{pmatrix} = 2c$ **3** $\begin{pmatrix} 4 \\ 6 \end{pmatrix}$

4 **(a)** $a + b$ **(b)** $\overrightarrow{PQ} = \frac{2}{5}b - \frac{4}{15}a$
  (c) No, it is not a multiple of b
5 **(a)** $2a$ **(b)** $3a + b$ **(c)** $2a + 2b$ **(d)** $\dfrac{3a}{2} + \dfrac{b}{2}$
6 **(a)** $y - x$
  (b) $\overrightarrow{QT} = 2y - 2x$ so $\overrightarrow{QT} \parallel \overrightarrow{PQ}$ and point Q is common, so PQT is a straight line.
7 **(a)** **(i)** $b - a$ **(ii)** $2a$ **(iii)** $2b - 2a$ **(b)** They are parallel.

Revision exercise 20

1 $17°$ **2** $x = 62°, y = 118°$
3 **(a)** $x = 47°$ **(b)** $y = 48°$
4 **(a)** $48°$ (alternate segment)
  (b) $70°$ (cyclic quadrilateral, $B\hat{C}D = 110°$)
  (c) $132°$ (angles in triangle)
  (d) $24°$ (angles in triangle with $B\hat{D}A = 62°$ and $B\hat{D}X = B\hat{X}D$, isosceles triangle)
5 $B\hat{E}D = B\hat{D}E$ $(BE = BD)$
  So $B\hat{D}E = \dfrac{180 - x}{2} = 90 - \dfrac{x}{2}$
  Similarly $C\hat{D}F = 90 - \dfrac{y}{2}$
  $B\hat{D}E + C\hat{D}F + E\hat{D}F = 180°$
  So $E\hat{D}F = \dfrac{x}{2} + \dfrac{y}{2}$ or $\dfrac{x + y}{2}$ or $\dfrac{1}{2}(x + y)$
6 **(a)** $2x$ **(b)** AB is a tangent to the circle at point B
      $BC = BD$
      ADC is a straightline
      Angle $ABD = x°$
7 **(a)** Angles at $\hat{P}$ and $\hat{Q} = 90°$, so $\hat{P} + \hat{Q} = 180°$. Hence $OPTQ$ is cyclic.
  (b) $14.2\,\text{cm}$

Revision exercise 21

1 **(a)** 19 **(b)** 19
2 Select, at random, a number between 1 and 20 – call it n. Sample nth, $(n + 20)$th, $(n + 40)$th, etc.
3 **(a)** 498 **(b)** 1224 **(c)** 1434

Revision exercise 22

1 $30.9\,\text{g}$
2 **(a)** $20 < t \leqslant 30$ **(b)** $18\,\text{min}$
  (c)
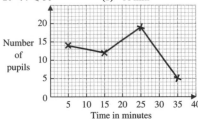

3 $285\,\text{g}$ **4** 1.2125 hours.

Revision exercise 23

1 **(a)**

	< 10	< 20	< 30	< 40	<50	< 60
Cf	20	38	44	48	50	52

(b)
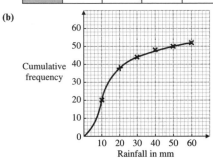

(c) Approx. $13\,\text{mm}$ **(d)** Approx. $13.5\,\text{mm}$
(e)
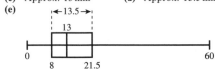
(f) 30.

2 **(a)**

	< 1.5	< 2.0	< 2.5	< 3.0	< 3.5	< 4.0	< 4.5	< 5.0
Cf	4	13	24	45	71	89	98	100

(b)
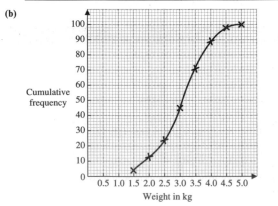

(c) Approx. 3.1 kg

(d)

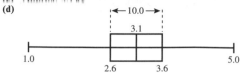

Approx 1 kg

(e) Approx. 60%

3 (a) Cumulative frequencies are 2, 3, 6, 14, 25, 29, 31

(b)

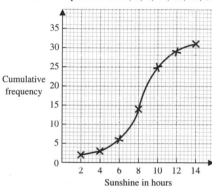

Cumulative frequency

Sunshine in hours

(c) Approx. 8.2 hours

(d) Approx. 3 hours

(e) Ashwell median > Downtown median and the two interquartile ranges are about the same.
So Ashwell generally had more sunshine.

4 (a) Cumulative frequencies are 10, 30, 65, 90, 98, 100.

(b)

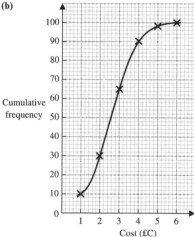

Cumulative frequency

Cost (£C)

(c) (i) £2.50 approx   **(ii)** £1.80 approx
(iii) £3.30 approx   **(iv)** 16% approx

Revision exercise 24

1 Frequency column is: 32, 20, 18, 4.

2 (a) Student's plot
(b) 103.5, 107, 108.5, 110, 112.5, 117, 119, 120.5, 123.5, 128, 129, 131, 133
(c) Student's plot   **(d)** There is a steady increase in the oil bills.

3 (a) Student's plot
(b) 118.4, 118.1, 119.7, 118.9, 119.4, 120.1, 124.6, 126.3, 125.6, 122.6, 129.1, 124.4, 126, 124.6, 122, 124, 123.7, 118.6, 121.3, 117.9, 118.4, 120.4
(c) Wednesday and Saturday

4 (a) Student's plot   **(b)** Student's plot
(c) The major trend is for an increase in house prices over this period.

5 (a) 5

(b)

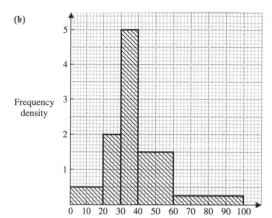

Frequency density

Number of hours (h)

6 (a) Student's plot
(b) 3.7, 3.8, 4.0, 3.9, 3.8, 3.9, 4.0, 4.2, 4.3, 4.3
(c) Student's plot
(d) The moving averages suggest that Jenny's bonus payments are increasing.

7

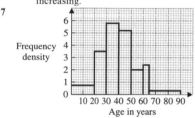

Frequency density

Age in years

Revision exercise 25

1 (a) 1600   **(b)** 0.4   **(c)** 0.1   **(d)** 0.98

2 (a)

(b) $\frac{8}{35}$ **(c)** $\frac{14}{35} = \frac{2}{5}$

3 $\frac{31}{72}$ **4** $\frac{23}{60}$ **5** 0.984   **6** $\frac{1}{32}$

Examination practice paper
Non-calculator

1 (a) £56   **(b)** £40   **2 (a)** $x = \frac{22}{3}$ **(b)** $\pm 3\sqrt{3}$

3 $\frac{150}{500} = \frac{3}{10}$ Best estimate $(62 + 88)$ out of 500 trials

4 $x = 3$, $y = -1$

5 $\angle BAD = 108°$ (cyclic quad)
$\angle BDA = 36°$ (angle in isosceles triangle ABD)
$\angle TAB = 36°$ (alternate angle)

6 $320 + 32\pi$ cm^2

7 (a) n^8 **(b)** $10x + 26$ **(c)** $5(a - 3)$ **(d)** $2xy(x^2 + 3y^2)$
(e) $x = -\frac{7}{5}$ **(f)** $(x - 7)(x + 4)$ $x = 7$ or $x = -4$

8 (a), (c)

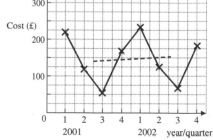

Cost (£)

year/quarter

(b) 143, 146, 148, 149.5, 152
(d) bill lowest in third quarter
bill highest in first quarter
steady increase

9   $(2n+1)^2 - (2n-1)^2 = (2n+1+2n-1)(2n+1-(2n-1))$
               difference of 2 squares
               $= 4n(2)$
               $= 8n$ therefore multiple of 8

10   **(a)** 75.6   **(b) (i)** $\frac{237}{999} = \frac{79}{333}$ **(ii)** $\frac{509}{990}$

11   **(a)** missing value from table = 16
    (b)

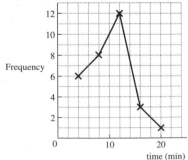

12   **(a)**   **(b)** $\dfrac{25\pi}{4}$

13   Student's own correct proof from $\dfrac{4\pi r^3}{3} = 2r$

14   $\dfrac{x+7}{(x-1)(x+7)}$

15   0.94

16   **(a)** Student's own correct proof from $ax + b = mx + c$
    (b) $c - b = 0$, $a - m = 0$ so x has no real value. Lines co-incident.

17   **(a) (i)** $\begin{pmatrix} -4 \\ -3 \end{pmatrix}$ **(ii)** 5 units   **(b)** $\begin{pmatrix} -2 \\ 8 \end{pmatrix}$ **(c)** $(-6, 5)$

18   **(a)** $(2x - y)(2x + y)$ **(b)** $x = 3\ y = 1$

19   **(a)** x^{nm} **(b)** 25   **(c)** 16^4; 4^{14}; 2^{29}; 32^7; 8^{12}

20   **(a)** $y = (x - 3)^2 + 2$ **(b)** $(3, 2)$

Examination practice paper
Calculator

1   67.25 cm
2   3.5
3   **(a)**

(b) 8 min   **(c)** $\frac{10}{30} = \frac{1}{3}$

4   **(a)** $(1, 5.5)$ **(b)** $y = -\dfrac{1}{2x} + 6$

5   **(a)** 3.75×10^4 **(b)** 1.65×10^5
6   **(a)** $1696.46\,\text{cm}^3$ **(b)** 11.93 cm
7   2.43

8   **(a)**

(b) (i) $\frac{16}{22}$ **(ii)** $\frac{89}{225}$ **(iii)** $\frac{104}{225}$

9   £2850.45 to nearest p

10

11   **(a)** 3, 21, 67, 99, 115, 119, 120
    (b)

(c) approx 16 cars (correct from student's graph)
(d)

12   54.3°
13   **(a)** Student's proof   **(b)** $x = \frac{3}{2}$ or -3
14   147.5 km
15   21 students
16   **(a)** 2.1579 (4 d.p.)   **(b)** 1.4634 (4 d.p.)
17   **(a)** 4   **(b)** $\pm\sqrt{10}$
18   **(a) (i)** 16.55 cm   **(ii)** 8 cm
    (b) 41.2°   **(c)** $140\,\text{cm}^3$
19   $5881.06\,\text{cm}^3$
20   **(a)** $x^2 = (x + 9)^2 - (x + 7)^2 = 4x + 32$ **(b)** $\frac{120}{17}$ or 7.06